Technical English 1

Workbook

Christopher Jacques

Pearson Education Limited

Edinburgh Gate
Harlow
Essex CM20 2JE
England

and Associated Companies throughout the world.

www.pearsonelt.com

© Pearson Education Limited 2008

First published 2008
Thirteenth impression 2022

ISBN: 978-1-4058-4548-9 (book)

ISBN: 978-1-4058-9652-8 (book for pack)

Set in Adobe Type Library fonts

Printed in Great Britain by Ashford Colour Press Ltd.

Acknowledgements

The publishers and author would like to thank the following for their invaluable feedback, comments and suggestions, all of which played an important part in the development of the course: Eleanor Kenny (College of the North Atlantic, Qatar), Julian Collinson, Daniel Zeytoun Millie and Terry Sutcliffe (all from the Higher Colleges of Technology, UAE), Dr Saleh Al-Busaidi (Sultan Qaboos University, Oman), Francis McNeice, (IFOROP, France), Michaela Müller (Germany), Małgorzata Ossowska-Neumann (Gdynia Maritime University, Poland), Gordon Kite (British Council, Italy), Wolfgang Ridder (VHS der Stadt Bielefeld, Germany), Stella Jehanno (Centre d'Etude des Langues/ Centre de Formation Supérieure d'Apprentis, Chambre de Commerce et d'Industrie de l'Indre, France) and Nick Jones (Germany).

Illustrated by Mark Duffin, Peter Harper and HL Studios

The publisher would like to thank the following for their kind permission to reproduce their photographs:

(Key: b-bottom; c-centre; l-left; r-right; t-top)

Alamy Images: CrashPA 8 (1); alveyandtowers.com: 8 (4); Andrew Holt Photography: 16bc; Art Directors and TRIP photo Library: 16t, 19; aviation-images.com: Mark Wagner 8 (3); Britain on View: Lee Mawdsley 38; Corbis: Bo Zaunders 8 (6); Charles O'Rear 42c; David Kimber: 9 (middle far left), 9 (middle left), 9 (middle right), 9 (middle far right), 9 (bottom far left), 9 (bottom left), 9 (bottom right), 9 (bottom far right), 9tl, 9tc, 9tr; DK Images: 16tl, 16r, 16bl; Eye Ubiquitous / Hutchison: Bob Battersby 52; Freeplay Energy: 15; Joel Brown www.syntheticimage.net: Joel Brown www.syntheticimage.net 8 (2); Los Alamos National Laboratory: 63; NASA: 40; PA Photos: 29; Michel Spingler 42b; PunchStock: Corbis 48 (4); Punchstock / Uppercut: 48 (1); Rex Features: Andy Lauwers 8 (5); Goran Algard 50; Image Source 48 (2), 48 (3); Robert Down: Robert Down / photographersdirect.com 32; Science Photo Library Ltd: TRL Ltd 28; Travel Library Ltd, The: Stuart Black 42t; Woods Hole Oceanographic Institution: 58

Cover image: *Front*: iStock Photo: Kristian Stensoenes

All other images © Pearson Education

Picture Research by: Kevin Brown

Every effort has been made to trace the copyright holders and we apologise in advance for any unintentional omissions. We would be pleased to insert the appropriate acknowledgement in any subsequent edition of this publication.

Designed by Keith Shaw

Cover design by Designers Collective

Project Managed by David Riley

Contents

Unit 1 Check-up

4   **1.1 Basics**
Meeting and greeting people
Following instructions
Verb be

5   **1.2 Letters and numbers**
Using forms
Units of measurement
How do you spell ...?

6   **1.3 Dates and times**
Using numbers
Talking about travel timetables
Making appointments
Five oh three, Wednesday the fifth of July

Unit 2 Parts (1)

8   **2.1 Naming**
Identifying things
this, that, these, those

9   **2.2 Assembling**
Saying what you need for a job
Using an instruction manual
Imperative + object + location

10 **2.3 Ordering**
Using voicemail
Ordering by phone
How many do you need?
What's your name? Please spell that.

12 **Review Unit A**

Unit 3 Parts (2)

14 **3.1 Tools**
Describing components
Present simple of have

15 **3.2 Functions**
Saying what things do
Describing a product
Present simple

16 **3.3 Locations**
Saying where things are
Adverbials and prepositions of location

Unit 4 Movement

18 **4.1 Directions**
Describing direction of movement
Adverbials of direction
can, can't, cannot

19 **4.2 Instructions**
Talking about speed
Giving instructions
Imperative + present simple

20 **4.3 Actions**
Using an instruction manual
Explaining what happens
When clause

22 **Review Unit B**

Unit 5 Flow

24 **5.1 Heating system**
Explaining how fluids move around a system
Present simple
Prepositions of movement

25 **5.2 Electrical circuit**
Explaining how an electrical circuit works
Zero conditional

26 **5.3 Cooling system**
Explaining how cooling systems work
Reference words: here, it, this
Present simple in routines

Unit 6 Materials

28 **6.1 Materials testing**
Giving a demonstration
Explaining what you're doing
Present continuous

29 **6.2 Properties**
Describing the properties of materials
Present simple

30 **6.3 Buying**
Using a customer call form
Buying and selling by phone
Checking
What's your email address?
Could you spell/repeat that?
How many would you like?

32 **Review Unit C**

Unit 7 Specifications

34 **7.1 Dimensions**
Specifying dimensions
How long is it? It's 9 mm long.
The sea has a depth of 270 metres

35 **7.2 Quantities**
Specifying materials
Buying materials for a job
Countable and uncountable nouns

36 **7.3 Future projects**
Describing plans for the future
will, won't
Time expressions

Unit 8 Reporting

38 **8.1 Recent incidents**
Taking an emergency call
Explaining what has happened
Checking progress
Present perfect

39 **8.2 Damage and loss**
Reporting damage
Dealing with a customer
Past participles as adjectives

40 **8.3 Past events**
Discussing past events
Phoning a repair shop
Past simple
Time expressions

42 **Review Unit D**

Unit 9 Troubleshooting

44 **9.1 Operation**
Explaining how things work and what things do
Revision of present simple

45 **9.2 Hotline**
Using a service hotline
Solving a customer's problem
Short answers

46 **9.3 User guide**
Using a troubleshooting guide
Zero conditional + imperative

Unit 10 Safety

48 **10.1 Rules and warnings**
Following safety rules and signs
Giving and following warnings
could, might, must
always... Don't... You mustn't...

49 **10.2 Safety hazards**
Giving and following warnings
Noticing safety hazards
Reporting safety hazards
Past tense of be

50 **10.3 Investigations**
Investigating an accident
Reporting an accident
Questions in the past simple

52 **Review Unit E**

Unit 11 Cause and effect

54 **11.1 Pistons and valves**
Expressing causation, permission and prevention
Gerunds and infinitives

55 **11.2 Switches and relays**
Explaining how a relay circuit works
Further practice of verb patterns in 11.1

56 **11.3 Rotors and turbines**
Explaining how a wind turbine works
Further practice of verb patterns in 11.1

Unit 12 Checking and confirming

58 **12.1 Data**
Describing specifications
Revision of question forms

59 **12.2 Instructions**
Following spoken instructions
Confirming actions
Describing results of actions
Revision of imperative with present continuous

60 **12.3 Progress**
Describing maintenance work
Revision of present perfect, past simple, present continuous, and will

62 **Review Unit F**

64 **Audioscript**

70 **Answer key**

1 Basics

1 Use the words in the box to complete the dialogues.

what's	where	what	I'm	is	are	I'm

1 A: Hi, _____ Kaito.

B: Hello, my name _____ Pedro.

A: Nice to meet you.

2 A: Hello. _____ are you from?

B: I'm from Japan. _____ is your name, please?

A: I'm Hans. Pleased to meet you.

3 A: Good to meet you, Svetlana. _____ you from Poland?

B: No, _____ from Russia. _____ your name?

A: I'm Danielle.

2 Use the words in the pool to complete the orders.

1 Stand _____.

2 Write _____.

3 Turn _____.

4 Close _____.

5 Sit _____.

6 Raise _____.

7 Come _____.

right

down

your name

your book

in

up

your hand

3 Write the words in the correct columns.

adapter	antenna	bolts	cable	chisel	nuts	plug	saw	screwdriver
screws	spanner	washers						

Tools	Electricals	Fixings
_____	*adapter*	_____
_____	_____	_____
_____	_____	_____
_____	_____	_____

2 Letters and numbers

1 ▶ 🌀 **02** Listen and correct the five mistakes on the business card.

2 ▶ 🌀 **03** Listen and complete the form.

3 Match items 1–10 with the right words. Then match items 11–20.

1 gal	a) amp
2 €	b) angle/degree
3 kg	c) Celsius
4 A	d) euro
5 in	e) foot
6 ft	f) gallon *1*
7 km	g) gram
8 °	h) inch
9 g	i) kilogram
10 C	j) kilometre
11 +	k) kilometres per hour
12 m	l) kilowatt
13 kW	m) litre
14 V	n) metre
15 kph	o) negative
16 rpm	p) positive *11*
17 W	q) pound
18 L	r) revolutions per minute
19 £	s) volt
20 –	t) watt

4 04 Mr Martin is buying a car. Listen and write down the facts about the car.

1 Kilometres: *120 000* km
2 Engine temperature: ________ ° Celsius
3 Petrol tank: ________ litres
4 Engine speed: up to ________ rpm
5 Top speed: ________ kph
6 Price: ________ euros

3 Dates and times

1 Write the words for these ordinal numbers.

4th	*fourth*	5th	________
12th	________	29th	________
23rd	________	8th	________
7th	________	31st	________
30th	________	6th	________
22nd	________	20th	________

2 Complete the puzzles.

1 Jan 31 Fri → Feb 8
January the thirty-first is a Friday, so February the eighth is a Saturday.

2 Mar 29 Wed → Apr 2
____

3 May 29 Tue → June 3
____

4 July 30 Thur → Aug 4
____

5 Sept 28 Mon → Oct 7
____

6 Nov 27 Thur → Dec 6
____

3 Use the words in the box to complete the dialogue.

that's is it's then what when's it's

A: ______ the meeting?
B: ______ on Monday.
A: ______ that Monday 12th?
B: Yes. ______ right.
A: Do you know ______ time?
B: ______ at 10 o'clock.
A: OK. See you ______. Bye.
B: Bye.

4 Word list

NOUNS	NOUNS	ORDINAL NUMBERS	VERBS
adapter	amp	first	listen
antenna	angle	second	lower
bolt	Celsius	third	pick up
cable	degree	fourth	put down
chisel	euro	fifth	raise
nut	foot	sixth	read
plug	gallon	seventh	say
saw	gram	eighth	sit
screw	inch	ninth	stand
screwdriver	kilogram	tenth	start
spanner	kilometre	eleventh	stop
washer	kilometres per hour	twelfth	write
counter	kilowatt	thirteenth	**ADVERBS**
flight	litre	twentieth	closed
model	metre	thirtieth	down
platform	pound	**PHRASES**	in
first name	revolutions per minute	Excuse me	left
surname	volt	Hello	off
initial(s)	watt	Good to meet you	on
	ADJECTIVES	Nice to meet you	open
	negative	Pleased to meet you	out
	positive		right
			up

1 Make up answers to these questions. Use words from column 2 of the Word list.

1 How heavy is it? *425 grams   22 kilograms*

2 How hot is it? _____

3 How long is it? _____   _____   _____

4 How far is it to Dubai? _____

5 How fast is the car travelling? _____

6 How fast is the engine turning? _____

7 How much petrol is in the tank? _____   _____

8 What's the price of the car? _____   _____

9 How do you write *225 V* in words?

_____

1 Naming

1 Write sentences for the pictures.

Parts	Vehicles
axle deck nose number plate tail wheel	boat motorbike mountain bike plane racing car rocket

1 *That's the wheel of a racing car.*

2 _____

3 _____

4 _____

5 _____

6 _____

2 Use the words in the box to correct the sentences.

bolts   nails   nuts   screw   screwdriver   spanner   staple   washers

1 *That isn't* **a hammer. That** *'s a screwdriver.*

2 *Those aren't* **screws. Those** *are nails.*

3 *This* _____ a chisel. This _____.

4 _____ washers. These _____.

5 _____ a nail. This _____.

6 _____ nuts. These _____.

7 _____ a staple. That's _____.

8 _____ nuts. Those _____.

2 Assembling

1 How do you change a car wheel? You need:

a **jack**, to raise and lower the car   a **box spanner**, for the nuts   a **spare wheel**

Complete the instructions for the pictures, using the verbs from the box.

loosen   lower   put on   raise   take off   tighten

1 _____ the car with the jack.
2 _____ all the nuts with the box spanner.
3 _____ all the nuts.
4 _____ the wheel _____ the axle.
5 _____ the spare wheel _____ the axle.
6 _____ all the nuts.
7 _____ all the nuts with the box spanner.
8 _____ the car.

2 Write the dialogue lines in the right order.

30 mil. How many nails do you need?	Shopkeeper: _____
30 mil, please.	Customer: _____
Hello.	Shopkeeper: _____
I need 80, please.	Customer: _____
Some nails. What size do you need?	Shopkeeper: _____
Hello. I need some nails, please.	Customer: _____

3 Ordering

1 ▶ 🎵 05 Listen to the two phone messages. Correct the mistakes in the names and numbers.

| 1 Name: Vladislaw Sczetin | Phone number: 00 48 920 4516 |
| 2 Name: Abdel Mohamed Mabruk | Phone number: 00 20 537 1490 |

2 ▶ 🎵 06 Listen to the two phone messages. Complete the message forms.

1

Date: _____

Time: _____

Caller: _____

Phone number: _____

2

Date: _____

Time: _____

Caller: _____

Phone number: _____

3 ▶ 🎵 07 Listen to the dialogue. A customer is ordering skateboard parts on the phone. Complete the order form.

SKATEBOARDERS							ORDER

Surname: _____

Address: _____

_____

Postcode: _____

Tel: _____

Item (circle)	Colour (circle)			Size (circle)			Quantity (write)
Helmet	red	yellow	blue	large	medium	small	_____
Deck	red	yellow	blue	large	medium	small	_____
Pad	red	yellow	blue	large	medium	small	_____

4 Word list

NOUNS	NOUNS	VERBS	ADJECTIVES
axle	bolt	assemble	large
deck	hammer	loosen	medium
helmet	lever	pull	small
nose	nail	push	red
pad	nut	put	yellow
plate	screw	take	blue
tail	screwdriver	tighten	
truck	spanner	use	
wheel	staple		
	washer		

1 Spelling: there are eight words in the Word list with double letters. Write them here.

wheel, _____

_____

2 Vocabulary groups: write the words in column 2 on the correct line.

Tools: *hammer*, _____

Things: *bolt*, _____

3 Complete the instructions for skateboarding with words from the box.

loosen   push   put   take   tighten

Before skateboarding

_____ on the helmet.

_____ it down onto your head.

_____ the helmet strap.

_____ on the pads.

_____ the pads.

After skateboarding

_____ the pads and _____ them off.

_____ the helmet strap and _____ off the helmet.

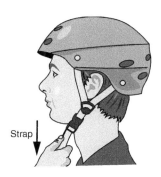

Strap

A | Review

Section 1

1 Complete the dialogues.

| I'm | he's | that's | is | do | I'm | are |

1 A: _____ you Maria?
   B: No, _____ Sonia. _____ Maria.

2 A: What _____ you do, Toni?
   B: _____ a builder.

3 A: _____ Carlos a builder?
   B: No, _____ an electrician.

2 Check the information in Students' Book page 9. Write the dates in column 2.

A person writes ...	What is the date?
1 Claire Paris, 1/2/11	February 1st 2011
2 Vicky Chicago, 3/9/11	_____
3 Yuki Tokyo, 11/01/22	_____
4 Matt Seattle, 11/12/11	_____
5 Director, ISO Geneva, 2011.07.08	_____
6 Peter Berlin, 9/10/11	_____

3 Work out the sequence of days and dates. Write the missing ones.

1 Monday, May the first
2 *Thursday, May the fourth*
3 Sunday, May the seventh
4 _____
5 Saturday, May the _____
6 _____
7 Friday, May the _____
8 _____

Section 2

1 Jumbled letters. Write the plural words.

1 lotsb   *bolts*   5 ilsan   n_____

2 hessraw   w_____   6 lesax   a_____

3 wressc   s_____   7 eatsksarbod   s_____

4 tuns   n_____

2 Write two more dialogues, like the example. Use the words from the box.

A: What's this tool called?

B: It's a *spanner*.

A: Is it for *nails*?

B: No. It's for *nuts*.

> hammer   screws   nuts   spanner   screwdriver   nails

A: What's this tool called?

B: It's _____

A: Is _____

B: _____

A: _____

B: _____

A: _____

B: _____

3 Complete the dialogue with the questions.

What's your phone number?   What's your email address?

What's your name?   What size cards do you need?

How many do you need?   What's your address and postal code?

When do you want them?

A: Hello. I need to order some business cards.

B: *How many* _____

A: 200, please.

B: _____

A: 85 millimetres by 55 millimetres.

B: _____

A: Stevens, with a V. Initials HC.

B: _____

A: 14 Hayfield Road, Bristol. BR7 4JK

B: _____

A: 0117 893462.

B: _____

A: It's harry.stevens@ojs.com

B: _____

A: Friday, please.

1 Tools

1 Complete the crossword. Find a twelfth word in the puzzle.

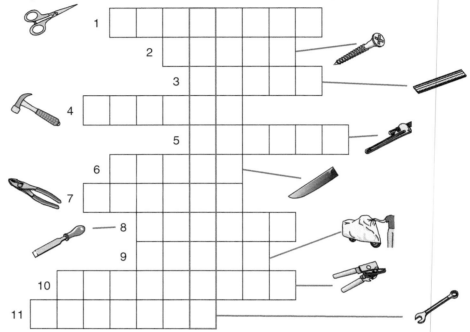

2 Write the answers to the puzzles. Use each item once.

> hammer   pair of pliers   pair of scissors   saw   screwdriver   spanner

1   It has a handle, a shaft and a head. It turns screws. It is a *screwdriver*.
2   It has a shaft and a head. It drives in nails. It is a _____.
3   It has two handles and two blades. It cuts paper. It is a _____.
4   It has a shaft and jaws, but no blades. It tightens nuts. It is a

_____

5   It has two handles, jaws and blades. It cuts wire. It is a _____.
6   It has a handle and a blade. It cuts wood. It is a _____.

3 Use the words in the box to complete the dialogues.

> do   does   don't   doesn't   have   has

1   A: _____ Carlos need a spanner?
    B: No, he _____.
    A: _____ he need a pair of pliers?
    B: Yes, he _____.
    A: Does he _____ a saw?
    B: Yes, he _____ two.

2   A: _____ you have a hammer?
    B: No, I _____.
    A: _____ you need a hammer?
    B: Yes, I _____.
    A: I don't _____ one. Go and ask Pedro. He _____ one in his tool box.

2 Functions

1 Match the word halves and write the words next to the explanations.

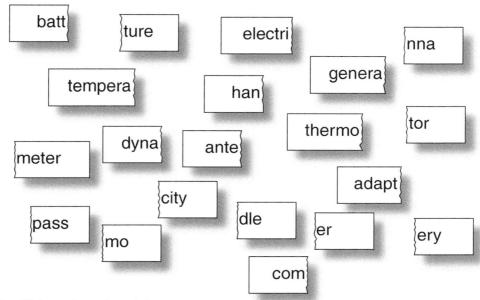

1 This makes electricity. *generator*
2 This shows North. _____
3 This stores electricity. _____
4 An AC _____ changes AC to DC.
5 This receives radio signals. _____
6 A solar panel changes sunlight into _____ .
7 You can measure _____ in Fahrenheit or Celsius.
8 You turn this round with your hand. _____
9 This measures temperature. _____
10 This turns and makes electricity. _____

2 Use the verbs from the box to complete the text.

charge   shine   charges   turn   listen   turns   produces

Are you going on holiday? This
3-in-1 torch, radio and battery
charger is for you.
When you (1)_____ the handle,
it (2)_____ the dynamo. This
(3)_____ the battery. You can
then (4)_____ the torch, or
(5)_____ to the radio.
For example, five minutes at 120
rpm (6)_____ enough power
to listen to the radio for twenty
minutes. You can also turn the
handle to (7)_____ your mobile
phone.

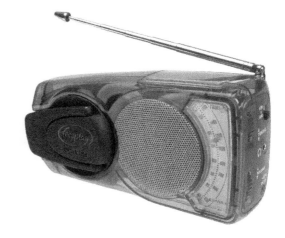

3 Locations

1 ▶ 🎵 **08** Listen to the dialogue in the factory. Where does the driver put the boxes?

1 speakers	2 keyboards	3 DVD players
4 scanners	5 headphones	6 amplifiers
7 mouse pads	8 adapters	9 printers

1 Listen and write the product number on the right shelf.

2 Write all the product names on the right shelves.

3 Look at the shelves. What order are the products in?

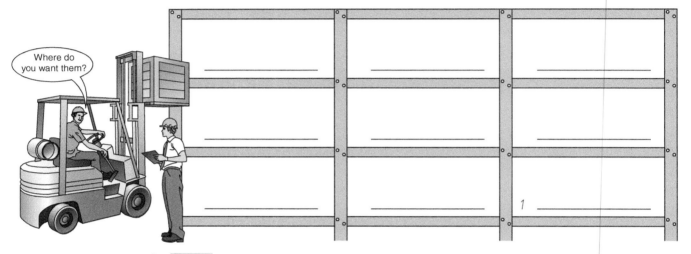

2 ▶ 🎵 **09** Listen to a dialogue on a boat. Where do the people put the things? Write the number of the location (1–12) next to the word on the right.

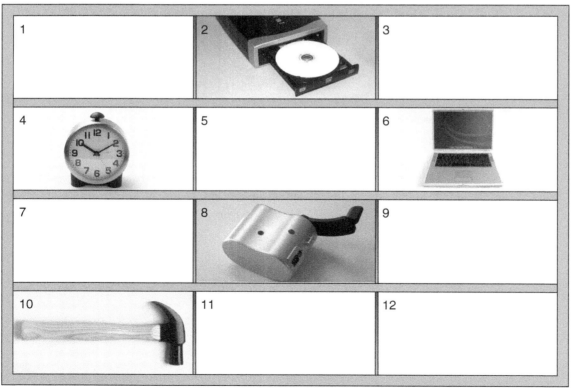

multi-tool
pliers
radio
wrench
batteries
torch
scissors *12*

4 Word list

NOUNS (tools)	NOUNS (electricity)	VERBS	ADJECTIVES
blade	alarm	change	external
boat	battery	charge	internal
bottle opener	clock	connect	plastic
building site	dynamo	cut	**PHRASES**
can opener	electricity supply	drive in	at the bottom
compass	generator	grip	at the top
cover	mains electricity	measure	in the centre
handle	radio	produce	in the middle
head	solar panel	receive	on the left
jaws	solar power	shine	on the right
key tool	torch	turn	above
metal	**NOUNS (computer)**		below
multi-tool	computer		to the left of
pick	computer station		to the right of
pliers	cursor		
ruler	DVD drive		
scissors	keyboard		
shaft	mouse		
string	printer		
survival tool	scanner		
thermometer	screen		
wire	speaker		
wrench			

1 Match each noun in column 1 with a phrase in column 2.

1	Chisels	a)	loosen screws.
2	Hammers	b)	tighten nuts.
3	Pliers	c)	cut wood.
4	Rulers	d)	drive in nails.
5	Saws	e)	cut metal.
6	Scissors	f)	grip wire.
7	Screwdrivers	g)	measure everything.
8	Wrenches	h)	cut paper.

4 | Movement

1 Directions

1 Look at the pictures of the jump jet.

    1   Which picture shows a vertical take-off? (Picture _____)

    2   Which picture shows a short take-off? (Picture _____)

    3   Which directions can you see? Write the letters from the pictures (A–D) here.

        vertically up _____   horizontal _____ diagonally up _____

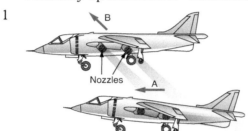

2 Which directions can the jump jet fly? Complete the text with words from the box.

forwards	sideways	straight down	straight up	to the right	up and down

The jump jet can fly like a helicopter or fly like a passenger plane. The jump jet has one engine and four nozzles. The four nozzles can point straight down. Then the jet engine lifts the plane (1)_____ into the air. In the air, the four nozzles can rotate and point backwards. This pushes the plane (2)_____. Then the plane can fly at about 1165 kph. Like a passenger plane, it can turn to the left or turn (3)_____. It can fly diagonally (4) _____. It can also fly backwards and (5)_____, a little. How does it land? It stops in the air and flies (6)_____.

3 Read about the movements of the human leg. Complete the text with words from the box.

angles	ankle	degrees	directions	hip	knee	move	pivots	rotate
sideways								

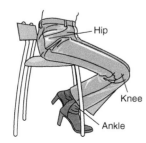

The leg has three (1) *pivots*, the hip, the knee and the ankle. The ankle can move in three (2)_____. At the (3)_____, the foot can move up and down about 50 (4)_____. It can (5)_____ from side to side about 50 degrees, and it can (6)_____ about 15 degrees. The (7)_____ can move in the same directions, but with different (8)_____. The (9) _____ can only move in one direction. At the knee, the lower leg can only move up and down. It cannot move (10)_____ or rotate.

2 Instructions

1 ▶ ⚙ **10** Write the full forms. Then listen and check.

1 30 kph *thirty kilometres per hour*

2 500 rpm _____

3 15 m/s _____

4 65 mph _____

5 8 km/s _____

2 ▶ ⚙ **11** Listen and write the speeds. Use the short forms from question 1.

1 Sound travels at _____.

2 The engine of a Formula 1 car turns at about _____.

3 The moon truck Apollo 16 Rover travels at _____.

4 A solar-powered car can travel at _____.

5 A person on skis can go downhill at _____.

6 A person on a snowboard can go downhill at _____.

7 The maximum speed of a train in France is _____.

8 The fastest sailing ship sails at _____.

9 A Blackbird jet flies at _____.

3 ▶ ⚙ **12** Listen to the dialogue. Are all the parts for the radio-controlled truck in the box? Listen and tick the things on the list.

Instruction manual

Transmitter

Truck

Antenna for transmitter

Antenna for truck

2 9V batteries

4 Use the words from the box to complete the text about the truck.

control   moves   press   receives   sends   turns   use

> The transmitter (1)_____ radio signals to the receiver in the truck. An antenna on the truck (2)_____ signals from the transmitter. The truck and the transmitter (3)_____ electricity from batteries. Six buttons (4)_____ the speed and direction: forwards, backwards, forward and left, forward and right, backwards and left, backwards and right. There are two electric motors. One motor (5)_____ the wheels to the left or right. The other motor drives the back wheels forwards or backwards. (6)_____ the control button 'Forwards'. The motor turns the shaft and the shaft turns the axle. The truck (7)_____ forward.

3 Actions

1 Read the instruction manual. Write the letters (A–H) from the diagram next to the names of the controls.

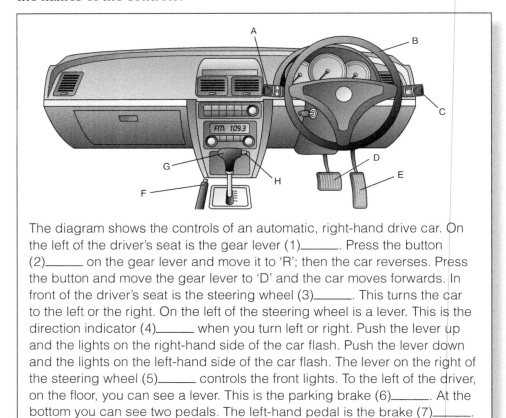

The diagram shows the controls of an automatic, right-hand drive car. On the left of the driver's seat is the gear lever (1)_____. Press the button (2)_____ on the gear lever and move it to 'R'; then the car reverses. Press the button and move the gear lever to 'D' and the car moves forwards. In front of the driver's seat is the steering wheel (3)_____. This turns the car to the left or the right. On the left of the steering wheel is a lever. This is the direction indicator (4)_____ when you turn left or right. Push the lever up and the lights on the right-hand side of the car flash. Push the lever down and the lights on the left-hand side of the car flash. The lever on the right of the steering wheel (5)_____ controls the front lights. To the left of the driver, on the floor, you can see a lever. This is the parking brake (6)_____. At the bottom you can see two pedals. The left-hand pedal is the brake (7)_____. The right-hand pedal is the accelerator (8)_____.

2 Write instructions for driving a car. Write full sentences from these notes. Use *when* and *you*, and add *the* and punctuation.

1 pull gear lever to 'R' → car reverses

When you pull the gear lever to 'R', the car reverses.

2 pull gear lever to 'D' → car moves forwards

_____

3 press accelerator → car goes faster

_____

4 press brake pedal a little → car goes slower

_____

5 turn steering wheel to the right → car turns right

_____

6 turn steering wheel to the left → car turns left

_____

7 press brake pedal → car stops

_____

3 Put the instructions for parking a car in the correct order. Complete the instructions with the following words: *forwards, left, right*.

Order: _____

A Drive _____ a little and turn the steering wheel to the _____.

B Reverse a little more and turn the steering wheel to the _____. Stop.

C Drive _____ slowly. Stop.

D Reverse and turn the steering wheel to the _____.

4 Word list

NOUNS (tools)	NOUNS (electricity)	VERBS	ADJECTIVES
accelerator	parking brake	accelerate	backwards
angle	pedal	ascend	down
antenna	pivot	control	forwards
brake	plane	descend	sideways
direction	revolution	dock	up
elbow	robot	park	to the left
forearm	roll	press	to the right
handle	shoulder	pull	**PHRASES**
helicopter	slider	push	horizontal axis
joystick	speed	reverse	vertical axis
kilometre	steering wheel	rotate	
lever	switch	slide	
metre	tilt	slow down	
mile	wrist	turn round	

1 Find nine nouns for driving a car. Write them here.

accelerator _____

_____

2 Find opposites in columns 3 and 4 for the following words and write them here.

accelerate   _____

ascend   _____

pull _____

forwards   _____

up _____

to the left   _____

3 Find seven verbs for flying a helicopter. Write them here.

Helicopters can accelerate, _____

_____

Section 1

1 Look at the diagram of the work station. Tick the true statements. Correct the false ones.

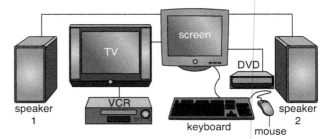

1 The screen is in the centre. ✓
2 The keyboard is in the centre, ~~above~~ the screen. *below*
3 The TV is to the right of the screen.
4 The VCR is on the left, below the TV.
5 Speaker 1 is on the right.
6 Speaker 2 is on the left.
7 The mouse is at the top, to the left of the keyboard.
8 The DVD drive is below the mouse, to the left of the screen.

2 Where are the programmes on the screen? Make sentences with the words in the box.

> bikes   cars   football   the news   boats   science   skateboards   space
> planes

1 *Football is at the top, on the left.*
2 *Planes are at the top, in the centre.*
3 _____
4 *Bikes are on the middle line,*
  _____
5 _____
6 _____
7 _____
8 _____
9 _____

3 Write the singular form of the words in the box. If a word has no singular form, write 'a pair of ...'.

> batteries   hammers   overalls   pincers   pliers   scissors   spanners   wrenches

1 Singular form: *battery* _____ _____
  _____

2 No singular form: *a pair of overalls* _____ _____
  _____

Section 2

1 Find letters in the diagram (A–D) for each sentence. Use the phrases from the box to complete the sentences.

> descend   up and down
> forwards and backwards
> rotate   diagonal or horizontal

1   (   ) The crane can move _____ on its wheels.

2   (   ) The top part of the crane can _____ through 360°.

3   (   ) The arm of the crane can ascend and _____ through 90°. It can be in a vertical, _____ position.

4   (   ) The hook below the end of the arm can go _____.

2 Use the words in the box to complete these questions and answers. Then match the questions with their answers.

> is   are   do   does   can   can't   put   need   press   goes   receives

1 _____ you find the user manual?
a) No, there _____ only one.

2 How _____ the truck work?
b) You _____ it in the transmitter.

3 Where _____ I put the battery?
c) No, I _____ find it.

4 Where _____ the antenna go?
d) Yes, we _____ it for the truck.

5 How _____ I steer the truck?
e) It _____ on top of the truck.

6 _____ there two batteries in the box?
f) It _____ signals from the transmitter.

7 _____ we need a second battery?
g) You _____ one of the control buttons.

3 Read the instructions (A–D) for steering a boat backwards. Put them in the correct order. Then complete the instructions with the following words: *forwards, left, centre, backwards.*

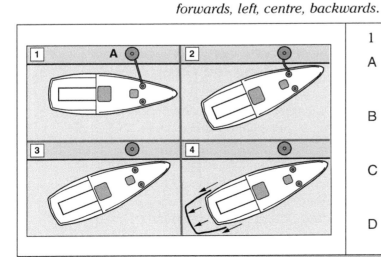

1   1 _____   2 _____   3 _____   4 _____

A   Turn the steering wheel to the _____ position. Pull the lever _____; this puts the engine into reverse. Reverse slowly.

B   Turn the steering wheel to the left. Push the engine lever forwards; this moves the boat slowly _____ and to the _____.

C   Pull the engine lever to the _____ position. Loosen the rope. Take off the rope from Point A.

D   Start the engine. Tie the rope on the _____ of the boat to Point A.

5 | Flow

1 Heating system

1 Draw a line from each word to its opposite.

sink   above   bottom   out of   cold   cool   enter   outlet   push

hot   inlet   leave   heat   pull   rise   top   below   into

2 Rewrite the sentences. Change the words in italics. Use words with opposite meanings from question 1.

1 A solar panel *heats* water. A fridge … → *A fridge cools water.*

2 *Hot* water *rises* to the *top* of a water tank. →
_____

3 The *inlet* pipe for *cold* water is *below* the pump. →
_____

4 Water *enters* the tank through the *inlet* pipe. →
_____

5 *Push* the shower head *into* the pipe. →
_____

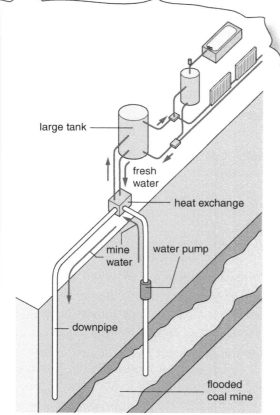

large tank

fresh water

heat exchange

mine water

water pump

downpipe

flooded coal mine

3 Look at the diagram. Warm water comes up from underground and heats water for the houses. Use the verbs and prepositions in the box to complete the description of the heating system.

flow	leave	push	rise	above
below	into	through	to	out of

In this system, there are houses (1) *above* a flooded coal mine. At 170 metres (2)_____ ground, the temperature of the mine water stays at 14.5 °C. The water pump brings up the mine water and (3)_____ it (4)_____ the heat exchanger. The mine water comes (5)_____ the heat exchanger and (6)_____ back into the coal mine (7)_____ the downpipe.

In the heat exchanger, the temperature of the fresh water (8)_____ to 55 °C. This warm water then flows to a large tank. Then it (9)_____ the large tank and goes (10)_____ the houses.

2 Electrical circuit

1 Match the words in the box to sentences 1–7.

> battery   cable   controller   lamp   solar panel   electrical current   switch

1   shines a light when the switch is on: *lamp*
2   converts the sun's energy into an electrical current: _____
3   stores electricity: _____
4   When a _____ is closed, the electrical current can flow.
5   DC is a type of _____.
6   Electricity passes through the _____ to the lamp or the battery.
7   carries the electrical current: _____

2   ▶ 🔵 **13** Look at the diagram for a water-wheel and a generator which supplies current to a workshop next to the river. Complete the sentences with the present simple. Then listen and check your answers.

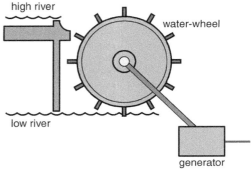

1   If the river is high, and the workshop is open, *the current flows from the generator into the workshop.* (current / flow / generator / workshop)
2   If the river is high, and the workshop is closed, _____ _____. (current / flow / generator / batteries)
3   If the river is low, and the workshop is open, _____ _____. (current / flow / batteries / workshop)
4   If the river is low, and the workshop is closed, _____ _____. (current / not / flow)
5   If the batteries are full, _____ _____. (current / not / flow / generator / batteries)
6   If the batteries are empty, _____ _____. (current / not / flow / batteries / workshop)

3   ▶ 🔵 **14** Listen to the dialogue. Circle the correct specifications for the items.

1	Solar panels	a) 4 × 16 W	b) 40 × 60 W	c) 4 × 60 W
2	Controller	a) 1 × 3 A	b) 1 × 5 A	c) 1 × 15 A
3	Batteries	a) 4 × 12 V, 50 Ah	b) 4 × 12 V, 100 Ah	c) 4 × 15 V, 150 Ah
4	Lamps	a) 6 × 20 V, 8 W	b) 16 × 12 V, 18 W	c) 6 × 12 V, 8 W
5	Cable (12 metres)	a) 2.5 mm, 30 amps	b) 6 mm, 53 amps	c) 16 mm, 100 amps

3 Cooling system

1 Complete these sentences for a world weather forecast. Write the temperatures as words.

1 The night-time temperature in Helsinki will be *minus two degrees Fahrenheit*. (–2 °F)

2 The day-time temperature in Mexico City will be *twenty-one degrees Celsius*. (21 °C)

3 The day-time temperature in Los Angeles will be _____. (75 °F)

4 The coldest night-time temperature in Moscow will be _____. (–8 °C)

5 The day-time temperature in Tunis will be _____. (24 °C)

6 The highest day-time temperature in Karachi will be _____. (33 °C)

2 Use the words in the box to answer the questions with short answers. Use some of the words twice.

cool water	engine	fan	hot water	thermostat	two hoses	water pump

1 What pushes cool water round the engine? *The water pump*

2 What connects the radiator to the engine? _____

3 What controls the temperature of the engine? _____

4 What flows from the engine to the radiator? _____

5 What blows air through the radiator? _____

6 What sinks to the bottom of the radiator? _____

7 What cools the water in the radiator? _____

8 What passes along the bottom hose and back to the engine? _____

9 What drives the water pump? _____

3 Look at the diagram for a watering system. Complete the sentences with the words in the box. Put the verbs into the present simple.

around	at the top	at the bottom	from	into	out of	through

1 From the spring, water (flow) *flows* to a reservoir *at the top* of the hill.

2 _____ the reservoir, water (pass) _____ _____ a pipe to the field.

3 The pipe (go) _____ _____ a field of fruit trees.

4 Water (leave) _____ the pipe _____ small holes.

5 The water then (flow) _____ _____ the fruit trees.

6 A little water (flow) _____ _____ the bottom of the field.

7 This water (enter) _____ a tank _____ of the hill.

spring

reservoir

fruit trees

field

tank

4 Word list

HEATING AND COOLING		PREPOSITIONS OF MOVEMENT	ELECTRICAL
NOUNS	VERBS		NOUNS
engine	blow	around	battery
fan	connect	into	cable
hose	control	out of	conductor
inlet	cool	through	controller
radiator	drive	to	electrical circuit
shower head	enter		electrical current
solar panel	flow		energy
thermostat	go		lamp
valve	heat		solar panel
water pipe	leave		switch
water pump	move		VERBS
water tank	pass		convert
	push		flow
	rise		shine
	sink		short-circuit

1 Complete the sentences with verbs from column 2.

1 Cold water _____ the system through the inlet.
2 Water _____ into the tank through a pipe.
3 The sun _____ the water in the solar panel.
4 Hot water _____ to the top of the tank.
5 Cold water _____ to the bottom of the tank.
6 Hot water _____ the system through the shower head.

2 Match the sentence halves.

1 The water pump pushes   a) the temperature of the water.
2 The thermostat controls   b) air through the radiator.
3 The two hoses connect   c) the hot water from the engine.
4 The fan blows   d) water around the engine.
5 The radiator cools   e) the radiator to the engine.

1 Materials testing

1 Make sentences about the materials with 'can ..., but ... can't', or 'can ... and ... can'.

1 (bend / metal / wood) *You can bend metal, but you can't bend wood.*

2 (heat / air / water) *You can heat air and you can heat water.*

3 (melt / plastic / wood)

_____

4 (scratch / glass / metal)

_____

5 (stretch / nylon / glass)

_____

6 (break / glass / wood)

_____

7 (cut / wood / metal)

_____

8 (compress / air / glass)

_____

2 A lecturer is showing a DVD of a test. Complete the description. Use the present continuous.

Hello. Now we can watch the DVD of a car crash. Here they (1)*are testing* (test) the material for the seatbelt. The human dummy (2)_____ (sit) in the test car. This dummy weighs 90 kilos. Here the technician (3)_____ (tighten) the nylon seatbelt around the dummy. Now the technician (4) _____ (start) the engine of the radio-controlled car.
Look at the crash in slo-mo (= slow motion). The car (5)_____ (run) into the concrete block at 40 kph. The body of the dummy (6)_____ (stretch) the nylon seatbelt. And see, the dummy (7)_____ (touch) the airbag. Look carefully. (8)___ the dummy's face _____ (strike) the front window? No, it isn't. There is no contact with the front window.

3 Write questions and answers for the pictures.

1 you / push / handles ?	2 he / walk ?	3 she / bend / wall bars ?
4 you / pull / bar / down ?	5 he / push / bar ?	6 she / bend / legs ?

1 A: *Are you pushing the handles?*   4   A:
   B: *No, I'm rowing.*   B:

2 A: 5   A:
   B: B:

3 A: 6   A:
   B: B:

2 Properties

1 Find the names of 14 materials in the puzzle and circle them. The words go vertically from top to bottom, and sideways from left to right. No words go diagonally.

B	A	J	L	O	Y	C	O	M	P	O	S	I	T	E
P	L	A	S	T	I	C	E	T	O	Z	P	R	A	K
L	U	R	T	I	B	K	Y	L	L	B	O	J	L	I
O	M	A	L	J	M	O	Q	A	Y	U	L	S	D	A
F	I	B	R	E	G	L	A	S	S	I	Y	T	I	Y
B	N	S	D	R	A	R	X	P	T	B	C	N	A	O
T	I	T	A	N	I	U	M	D	Y	F	A	H	M	I
J	U	E	K	Y	L	B	N	T	R	I	R	V	O	Z
A	M	E	B	L	C	B	F	G	E	A	B	H	N	I
J	R	L	K	O	Q	E	S	V	N	U	O	Z	D	W
Y	Z	C	O	N	C	R	E	T	E	X	N	B	G	Y
H	I	R	J	T	K	U	L	C	E	R	A	M	I	C
S	V	N	X	P	G	R	A	P	H	I	T	E	Q	W
I	Y	B	T	L	E	K	O	E	U	J	E	C	D	I

2 Underline the two correct adjectives for each material.

1 A ceramic cup is flexible/<u>heat-resistant</u> and <u>hard</u>/soft.

2 A concrete floor is rigid/flexible and brittle/tough.

3 A rubber tyre is rigid/flexible and weak/strong.

4 A fibreglass window frame is heat-resistant/soft and rigid/flexible.

5 A nylon rope is rigid/flexible and strong/weak.

6 The graphite in the middle of a pencil is light/heavy and hard/soft.

7 A polycarbonate road sign is rigid/flexible and strong/weak.

8 A polystyrene coffee cup is brittle/tough and heavy/light.

3 Design a plane. Choose one material for each part of the plane.

1 (nose cone / plastic / aluminium)
   The nose cone is made of aluminium.

2 (wheels / fibreglass / aluminium alloy)
   _____

3 (tyres / ceramic / rubber composite)
   _____

4 (frame / composite / polystyrene)
   _____

5 (inside / fibreglass / rubber composite)
   _____

6 (seats / plastic / ceramic)
   _____

7 (engine / fibreglass / aluminium alloy)
   _____

8 (wings / aluminium alloy / plastic)
   _____

3 Buying

1 ▶ **⊘ 15** Listen and complete the order form. A customer is buying equipment on the phone.

THE CLIMBING SHOP	
ORDER FORM	
Date: *23/03/08*	**Helmet** (polycarbonate / fibreglass) (L / M / S)
Product name: _____	
Product no: _____	**Rope** (nylon / nylon + rubber composite) (50 m / 75 m / 100 m)
Quantity: _____	
Colour: _____	**Jacket** (cotton / polyester) (XL / L / M / S)
Size: _____	
Material: _____	**Backpack** (nylon / polyester) (XL / L / M / S)
Price: _____	

2 ▶ **⊘ 16** Listen and correct the email addresses.

1 jclark@eyeway.co.uk → _____
2 alex2@antigm.ac.uk → _____
3 s.hagen@renault.fra → _____

3 ▶ **⊘ 17** Listen and write the website addresses.

1 News: _____
2 Live radio: _____
3 Radio-controlled toys: _____

4 A customer is phoning a sports shop. Write questions for the answers.

1 Q: *What's your surname, please?*
   A: It's Badrawi.
2 Q: _____
   A: B–A–D–R–A–W–I.
3 Q: _____
   A: 01273 497 633.
4 Q: _____
   A: Ali dot badrawi at atlas dot com.
5 Q: _____
   A: Yes. A–L–I dot badrawi at atlas, that's A–T–L–A–S dot com.
6 Q: _____
   A: I need three helmets.
7 Q: _____
   A: I'd like white ones, please.
8 Q: _____
   A: I want to pay in euros, please.

4 Word list

NOUNS (Materials)	NOUNS (Car parts, other)	VERBS	ADJECTIVES
alloy	backpack	bend	brittle
aluminium	cone	break	corrosion-resistant
ceramic	engine	burn	flexible
composite	frame	climb	hard
concrete	helmet	coat	heat-resistant
cromoly	jacket	compress	heavy
diamond	piston	corrode	light
fibreglass	radiator	drop	rigid
graphite	rope	heat	soft
nylon	spoiler	hold	strong
plastic	tyre	melt	tough
polycarbonate	vehicle	row	weak
polyester	wheel	run	**PHRASES FOR EMAILS**
polystyrene	wing	scratch	
rubber		stretch	dash
steel		strike	dot
titanium		touch	forward slash
			hyphen
			underscore

1 Memory test. What is a racing car made of? Write the materials from column 1.

1 The nose cone *is made of fibreglass.*

2 The wheels *are made of* _____
_____.

3 The frame _____.

4 The tyres _____.

5 The radiator _____.

6 The engine _____.

7 The pistons are coated with _____.

8 The wings are made of _____ and
_____.

2 Write the opposites of the adjectives from the list in column 4.

1 Nylon isn't weak. It's *strong.*

2 Polystyrene isn't tough. It's _____.

3 Graphite isn't hard. It's _____.

4 Rubber isn't rigid. It's _____.

5 Aluminium isn't heavy. It's _____.

Section 1

1 Use the words from the box to complete the phone dialogues.

> about   are   here   here   how   I'm   OK   thanks   that   this

1 A: Hello?
   B: Hello. Is (1)_____ Paulo?
   A: Yes.
   B: It's Sven (2)_____.
   A: Oh, hi, Sven.
   B: Hi. How (3)_____ things?
   A: Great, (4)_____. How are you?
   B: I'm (5)_____.

2 A: Hello. Mona Hall (6)_____.
   B: Oh, hi, Mona. (7)_____ is Ingrid.
   A: Hi, Ingrid.
   B: Hi. (8)_____ are you?
   A: Very well. How (9)_____ you?
   B: (10)_____ fine, thanks.

2 Write the -ing forms of the verbs on the correct line.

> bend   climb   cut   dive   drive   drop   grip   heat   hold
> leave   move   pull   push   rise   run   sit   strike   swim

1 Add *-ing*: *bending*, _____
   _____

2 Double the last letter and add *-ing*: *cutting*, _____
   _____

3 Drop the -e and add *-ing*: *diving*, _____
   _____

3 Complete the dialogue about the engine's cooling system. Put the verbs into the present continuous. One verb is used twice.

> blow   drop   go   push   rise   run   work

A: Is everything OK?
B: No. The engine's cooling system *isn't working*. The temperature of the water _____.
A: _____ the fan _____ air through the radiator?
B: Yes, the fan is fine.
A: _____ the pump _____ water round the engine?
B: Yes, the pump is working.
A: Look! That clip on the bottom hose is loose. Water _____ out of the hose. So the cold water _____ not _____ back to the engine. Tighten the clip.
B: _____ the water _____ out of the hose now?
A: No. Check the temperature.
B: Ah! The temperature _____. Good!

Section 2

1 Match phrases from the table to make sentences.

warm ice cubes	sink
pull a rubber band	burn
strike a ceramic cup very hard	break
heat water to 100 °Celsius	stretch
cool water	melt
heat pieces of wood	boil

If you warm ice cubes, they melt.

_____

_____

_____

_____

_____

2 Read the text and complete the table below.

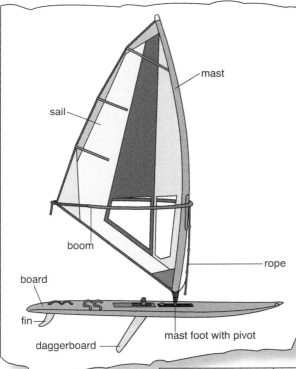

This sailboard is made from light, strong and flexible materials. The board is strong but light. It is made of polystyrene, coated with fibreglass. The mast is strong and flexible. It is made of polycarbonate. The mast and the boom support the sail. The boom is rigid and strong. It is made of aluminium, coated with rubber. The sail is light but strong. It is made of a mixture of nylon and polyester. Fixed to the end of the boom is a strong rope. It is made of nylon. The rigid daggerboard and fin are made of polycarbonate. There is a pivot at the foot of the mast. This is strong and flexible. It is made of rubber.

Part	Material	Properties
board	*polystyrene, fibreglass*	*strong, light*
mast		
boom		
sail		
rope		
daggerboard		
fin		
pivot		

1 Dimensions

1 Use the words in the box to label the picture.

| bridge | cable | deck | pier | pylon | road | span | tunnel |

A bridge
B _____
C _____
D _____
E _____
F _____
G _____
H _____

2 Make sentences. Write the words in the correct order.

1 270 has metres The sea of depth a → *The sea has a depth of 270 metres.*

2 deep is metres 25 river The → _____

3 is metres 330 span long The → _____

4 a 160 The height metres of have pylons → _____
_____

5 the 22 kilometres length The road of is → _____
_____

6 width has 8 deck The metres of a → _____

3 Write questions and answers about the bridge.

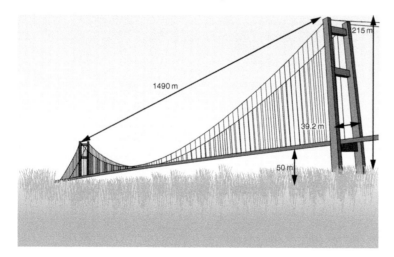

Runyang Bridge, China

1 where / this bridge ?
Q: *Where is this bridge?*
A: *It's in China.*

2 long / inner span ?
Q: _____
A: _____

3 high / pylons ?
Q: _____
A: _____

4 wide / deck ?
Q: _____
A: _____

5 high / deck / above water ?
Q: _____
A: _____

2 Quantities

1 Complete the text with facts from the specification chart.

The Gherkin

Address: 30 St Mary Axe, London
Completion date: 2003
Height: 180 m
Floors: 40
Glass area: 24 000 sq m
Floor area: circle
Footprint: small
Number of lifts: 18
Speed of lifts: 6 m/s
Materials: reinforced concrete,
    steel, aluminium, glass
Width of glass lens: 2.4 metres

This building is called 'The Gherkin'. It was completed in (1)_____. The (2)_____-storey building is 180 (3)_____ high. The building is made of (4)_____, (5)_____, (6)_____ and (7)_____. The glass windows have an (8)_____ of 24 000 (9)_____. The building has (10)_____ lifts. Each lift travels at 6 (11)_____. Each floor area of the building is a (12)_____. The floors at the top and bottom are small. The floors in the middle of the building are bigger. The footprint of the building is (13)_____. All the glass on the side of the building is flat. But on the top of the building, there is one round glass lens. It is 2.4 metres (14)_____.

2 ▶ 🎧 18 A customer is ordering some materials. Listen and complete the order form.

Item	Kind (circle)	Size (circle)	Product number (circle)	Quantity (write)
Paint	green / grey	5 / 10 litre tin	P176GR / D186G	
Cement	grey / white	10 / 20 kg bag	C0116W / S0196G	
Nails	packet of 50 / 100	24 / 30 mm	N420 / N240	
Screws	packet of 50 / 100	20 / 24 mm	S00941 / F00921	

3 ▶ 🎧 19 Listen and complete the questions from question 2.

1 *How much paint* do you need?
2 _____ _____ _____ do you need?
3 _____ _____ _____ do you need?
4 _____ _____ _____ do you need?
5 _____ _____ _____ do you need?
6 Do you have _____ _____?
7 _____ _____ _____ do you need?
8 Do you need _____ _____?

3 Future projects

1 Read the article about a new train tunnel. Complete the specification chart.

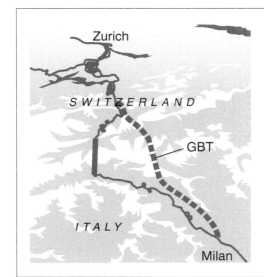

Zurich

SWITZERLAND

GBT

ITALY

Milan

The Gotthard Base Tunnel

The Gotthard Base Tunnel (GBT) will be the longest railway tunnel in the world. Engineers are building it now, in Switzerland, under the Alps. They will finish the project in 2016–2017.

Today, many trucks use the roads over the Alps. In future, they will use the GBT. The tunnel will connect Zurich in Switzerland with Milan in Italy.

There will be two tunnels. Each tunnel will be about 57 km long. They will run about 600 metres below the old St Gotthard railway tunnel (completed in 1881).

The new trains will use electricity. Some trains will carry trucks and cars. Fast passenger trains will travel at 250 kph. About 200–250 trains per day will use the GBT.

Gotthard Base Tunnel (GBT)	
Location of tunnel	*in Switzerland, under the Alps*
Possible completion date	
Number of tunnels	
Length of tunnels	
Depth below old tunnel	
Maximum speed of trains	
Source of power for trains	
Number of trains per day	

2 Change the long forms to short forms.

1 They are building a new tunnel. *They're building a new tunnel.*
2 There will be two new tunnels. _____
3 They will finish the tunnel in 2017. _____
4 The trains will not use magnetism. _____
5 There will be more than 200 trains per day. _____

3 Underline seven mistakes in this report. Then rewrite the report.

> The GBT will be the longest <u>road</u> tunnel in the world. It will connect Italy and France. Engineers will finish the project in 2011. The new tunnel will be above the old railway tunnel. There will be over 300 trains per day. The new trains will use diesel. All of them will run at 250 kph.

The GBT will be the longest railway tunnel _____
_____
_____
_____

4 Word list

NOUNS (Bridge)	NOUNS (Design)	NOUNS (Materials)	VERBS
cable	completion	aluminium	attach
deck	depth	cement	build
pier	design	fibreglass	fix
pylon	elevator	glass	lay
span	footprint	glue	make
NOUNS (Tunnel)	foundation	oil	put
compressed air	height	paint	**ADJECTIVES**
diesel	length	reinforced concrete	amazing
magnetism	location	steel	approximate
vacuum	material	superglue	deep
	quantity	**UNIT NOUNS**	high
	specification	bag	inner
	storey	bottle	long
	structure	packet	outer
	width	tin	super-fast
		tube	wide

1 Find nouns for these adjectives.

long – l_____   high – h_____   wide – w_____   deep – d_____

2 Make phrases from the words in the box. Write them below.

a	bottle tube bag packet tin	of	cement oil paint glue / superglue screws

_____   _____

_____   _____

_____

3 Choose a verb from the Word list and complete these phrases.

1 *lay* the foundations

2 _____ the piers

3 _____ the pylons on the piers

4 _____ the cables to the pylons

5 _____ the deck

6 _____ the deck to the cables

7 _____ the road

1 Recent incidents

1 Complete the table of verb forms.

		Verb	Past simple	Past participle
Type A Regular	add -ed	check		
	add -d			changed
Type B Regular	double the final letter and add -ed		stopped	
		plan		
Type C Irregular	verb = past simple = past participle	cut		
			put	
Type D Irregular	past simple = past participle		bought	
				sold
			sent	
Type E Irregular	past simple ≠ past participle		fell	
		speak		
				taken
		write		

2 Complete the dialogue. A is the manager. B is the manager's assistant.

A: *Have you spoken* to Security?

B: Yes, I have.

A: Good. _____ the new customer?

B: No, I haven't. I'll do it now.

A: _____ an email to HTB?

B: Yes, _____.

A: Good. _____ the incident report?

B: No, _____. I'll do it now.

> THINGS TO DO
> speak to Security ✓
> ring the new customer
> send an email to HTB ✓
> write incident report

3 Yesterday, the police received a lot of phone calls. Complete the sentences with verbs and nouns from the box.

have stolen has crashed has broken	diamonds digger motor boat shop
have come has taken have jumped	river town centre shop window
has driven have run	sledgehammer window

1 Hello? Police? A thief *has taken* my *digger*.

2 Police? A man _____ a digger into the _____ here.

3 Hello? A digger _____ into a

_____ in Broad Street.

4 Help! Two men _____ into my
_____ in Broad Street.

5 One man _____ the display case with a
_____.

6 The two thieves _____ some
_____.

7 Two men with bags _____ down to the
_____.

8 The two men _____ into a
_____. They are on the river now.

2 Damage and loss

1 ▶ 🔊 20 In each sentence, fill in the gap and underline the best verb. Then listen, check and repeat.

1 They *have* <u>bent</u> / burnt the router antenna.
2 The user manual *is* <u>torn</u> / burnt.
3 Someone _____ bent / broken the camera.
4 The body of the radio _____ cracked / cut.
5 The speakers _____ damaged / torn.
6 Someone _____ cut / bent the power cable.
7 The lenses of the goggles _____ cut / scratched.
8 I _____ burnt / broken my overalls.
9 They _____ dented / torn the car door.

2 ▶ 🔊 21 Listen to Part 1 of the dialogue and correct the customer details. Then listen to Part 2 and complete the damage report.

Order No:	PC08/1020/0017	Item	Damaged	Missing
Name:	Mr Bert Sandle	1 router antenna	*bent*	
Address:	14 Hayford Road	2 mouse		✓
	Catford	3 computer screen		
	London	4 keyboard		
Postcode:	SE10 4QU	5 power cable		
Tel:	0208 411 4009	6 LH speaker		
Email:	bsandell87@bdg.co.uk	7 RH speaker		
		8 user manual		

3 Complete the sentences. Some of the phrases are used more than once.

are   doesn't have   has   is   there's   there are

Reporting damage	Reporting something missing
1 The box *is* damaged.	1 The headphones _____ missing.
2 The overalls _____ torn.	2 _____ no pliers in the toolbox.
3 _____ a dent on one of the speakers.	3 The power cable _____ a plug.
4 _____ some cracks on the body of the radio.	4 _____ no batteries in the box.
	5 The radio _____ no antenna.
	6 _____ no user manual in the box.

3 Past events

1 Read the diary of a space tourist. Then complete the interview below.

1 Q: which year / travel / to / ISS?
   Which year did you travel to the ISS?
   A: In 2008.

2 Q: when / you / take off ?
   _____
   A: On April 12th.

3 Q: how / travel / into space ?
   _____
   A: On the Space Shuttle.

4 Q: what / take / with you ?
   _____
   A: Six Luka cameras and my laptop.

5 Q: what / do / on / ISS ?
   _____
   A: I tested all the Luka cameras.

6 Q: you / repair / solar panel ?
   _____
   A: No. John repaired it.

7 Q: when / you / leave / ISS ?
   _____
   A: On April 20th.

8 Q: when / you / land / in / USA ?
   _____
   A: On April 21st.

> 12.04.08 Took off on Space Shuttle. Took 6 Luka cameras and laptop.
> 13.04.08 Shuttle docked with International Space Station (ISS)
> 14.04.08 Tested all 6 Luka cameras. All worked OK.
> 15.04.08 John did spacewalk. He repaired solar panel on ISS.
> 20.04.08 Left ISS, after 7 days.
> 21.04.08 Returned to earth. Landed in USA.

2 Ben damaged his laptop a month ago. He rang the IT hotline. Write his answers to the questions. Use the past simple + *ago*.

1 When did you buy your laptop? (10 months)
   I bought it 10 months ago.

2 When did you drop it? (4 weeks)
   _____

3 When did you phone the company? (3 weeks)
   _____

4 When did you bring it into the Service Department? (10 days)
   _____

5 When did you send your email? (3 days)
   _____

6   When did you receive our bill? (2 days)

_____

7   When did you ring? (10 minutes)

_____

4 Word list

VERBS (Irregular)	VERBS (Regular)	VERBS (Damage)	NOUNS (Building)
bend / *bent*	check	bend	beam
break	climb	break	brick
burn	crack	burn	bucket
buy	crash	crack	builder
cut	dent	cut	crane
drive	happen	dent	digger
fall	land	scratch	hard hat
fly	launch	tear	scaffolding
go	lift	**NOUNS (General)**	sledgehammer
lose	move	accident	**NOUNS (Space)**
put	order	ambulance	global navigation
sell	raise	body (of radio)	moon
send	repair	damage	satellite
speak	scratch	display screen	shuttle
steal	snorkel	fuse	space station
take	**PHRASAL VERBS**	goggles (plural)	space tourist
tear	break into (irregular)	insulation	space walk
write	pick up (regular)	lens	telescope
	put on (irregular)	overalls (plural)	
	take off (irregular)	spark plug	
		surface	

1   Write the past tenses of all the irregular verbs on the Word list. (See the example at the top of column 1.)

2   Complete the sentences with nouns from the Word list.

1   They put the i_____ around the water pipe.

2   He climbed up to the top of the s_____.

3   He broke the bricks with a s_____.

4   He put a h_____ h_____ on his head and started work.

5   The c_____ lifted the metal beam onto the building.

6   One of the builders drove the d_____ into a brick wall.

7   He had an accident. He didn't put on his g_____ and damaged his eyes.

8   He stopped work, took off his dirty o_____ and went home.

Section 1

1 Use the words in the box to complete the texts. Some words are used more than once.

at	below	deep	depth	length	long	more than	through	wide	width

The Corinth Canal

The Corinth Canal is in Greece. It is 6.8 kilometres (1)_____ and 21 metres (2)_____. The (3)_____ of the water in the canal is 8 metres. Large ships cannot sail (4)_____ the canal, but small tourist ships can. (5)_____ 11 000 ships travel through the canal every year.

The TauTona Gold Mine

The TauTona gold mine is in South Africa. It has a maximum (6)_____ of 3.5 km. The total (7)_____ of tunnels is (8)_____ 800 km. Mine workers get to the bottom of the mine in super-fast lifts. These travel (9)_____ 16 m/s.
The mine opened in 1957. Soon they will open a new mine. This will be 3.9 km (10)_____.

The Channel Tunnel

The Channel Tunnel is a railway tunnel between England and France. It has two tunnels for trains. Each tunnel is 51.5 km (11)_____ and 7.7 metres (12)_____. There is a small third tunnel for engineers. This has a (13)_____ of 4.8 metres. The under-sea part of the tunnel has a (14)_____ of 39 km. Most of the tunnel is 45 metres (15)_____ the sea floor. The travel time (16)_____ the tunnel is 20 minutes. Tunnels were started in 1881 and in 1922. The present tunnel was completed in 1994.

2 Use the words in the box to complete the dialogues.

any	how	many	many	much	one	six	some	some

1 A: Hello. Can I help you?

   B: Yes. I'm building a wall and I need _____ cement.

   A: _____ much do you need?

   B: I need two bags please. And I also need _____ sand.

   A: How _____ bags do you need?

   B: I need _____ bags, please.

2 A: Hello. What can I do for you?

   B: Do you have _____ paint?

   A: Yes. How _____ do you need?

   B: 10 litres, please. And I need some nails.

   A: How _____ packets?

   B: _____ packet, please.

Section 2

1 Complete the table.

Verb	Past simple	Past participle
bend	*bent*	*bent*
build		
burn		
find		
lose		
pay		
break	*broke*	*broken*
come		
give		
go		

2 Ask questions about these recent incidents. Use the words in brackets.

1   A digger has driven into a shop window. (when / the / the)
    When did the digger drive into the shop window?

2   Some thieves have broken into the office. (when / the)
    _____

3   A mechanic has found some money. (how much / the)
    _____

4   Some builders have taken off the old roof. (when / the)
    _____

5   Some scaffolding has fallen down. (where / the)
    _____

3 Complete the dialogue. A is the supervisor. B is the builder.

A: *Have you put up the scaffolding?*
B: *Yes, I have.*
A: *Good. Have you changed the power cable?*
B: *No, I haven't. I'll do it next week.*
A: _____
B: _____
A: _____
B: _____
A: _____

THINGS TO DO
put up scaffolding ✓
change the power cable ✗
buy the bricks ✗
speak to the supplier ✓
order the water tank ✗

1 Operation

1 Use the words in the box to complete the text.

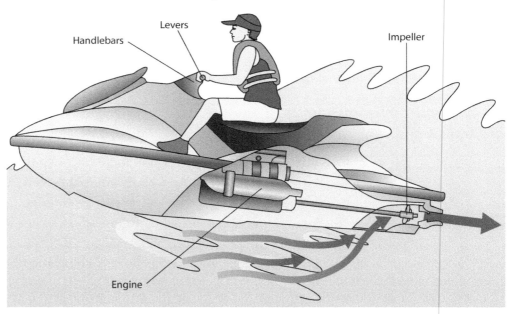

controls   drives   propels   pulls   pushes   release   steers   supports

Personal watercraft

A personal watercraft has a fibreglass body and an engine. A seat is mounted on the body and (1) *supports* the rider. The rider (2)_____the craft with handlebars and (3)_____ the speed with levers. The engine is mounted on the body of the craft and (4)_____ the impeller. The impeller (5)_____ water in and (6)_____ it out. This (7)_____ the craft forwards. If you want to stop the craft, you (8)_____ the lever. This stops the engine.

2 Complete the questions and answers.

1   What *does* the engine do?   It _____.
2   What _____ the impeller do?   It _____.
3   What _____ the handlebars do?   They _____.
4   What _____ the levers do?   _____
5   What _____ the seat _____?   _____

3 Make sentences with the words. Use 'mounted on' or 'attached to'.

1   seat / body   *The seat is mounted on the body.*
2   handlebars / body   _____
3   levers / handlebars   _____
4   engine / body   _____

2 Hotline

1 Find these things in the picture in question 2. Write the words below.

adapter   disk drive   display   mouse   power switch   speaker

1 *display*   3 _____   5 _____
2 _____   4 _____   6 _____

2 ▶ ⊙ **22** Listen to three short dialogues between a customer and a service technician. Parts of some of the dialogues don't match the picture. Listen and circle your answers.

Dialogue 1: no mistakes / 1 mistake / 2 mistakes

Dialogue 2: no mistakes / 1 mistake / 2 mistakes

Dialogue 3: no mistakes / 1 mistake / 2 mistakes

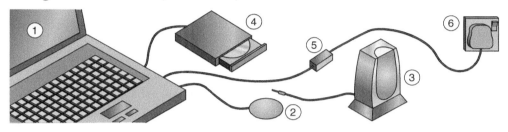

3 Look at the picture in question 2. Correct these sentences.

1   The display is closed. → *The display* _____.

2   The power switch is up. → _____

3   The mouse is disconnected. → _____

4   The speaker is connected. → _____

4 ▶ ⊙ **23** Use the words in the box to complete the dialogues. Then listen and check.

is   isn't   are   aren't   does   doesn't   do   don't

---

1   *Does* the computer start?
    No, it _____.
    Right. Press the power button again.

2   _____ the power switch down?
    No, it _____.
    OK. Press it down.

3   _____ the loudspeakers connected?
    No, they _____.
    OK. Connect them.

4   _____ the adapter connected?
    Yes, it _____.
    Good.

5   _____ the loudspeakers work?
    No, they _____.
    OK. Connect them and try again.

6   _____ the two LED lights on?
    Yes, they _____.
    Good.

7   _____ the computer start?
    Yes, it _____.
    Good.

8   _____ the loudspeakers work now?
    Yes, they _____.
    Good.

3 User guide

1 Read the Troubleshooting Guide. Underline the correct words.

Travelling with your notebook computer

Close / <u>Open</u> the display.

Press / Turn the power button.

If the display light is low, check / replace the LED for the battery.

If the battery is low, connect / recharge it.

If the battery still doesn't work / start, replace it.

At the end, to turn off your computer, touch / press the power button.

Close / Open the display.

2 Make sentences with 'if' from the dialogues.

1 Are the LEDs on? No, they aren't. OK. Check the battery.	3 Is the printer light on? No, it isn't. OK. Push the 'On' button.	5 Do the speakers work? No, they don't. OK. Connect them to the computer.
2 Does the printer work? No, it doesn't. OK. Connect it to the adapter.	4 Are the batteries old? Yes, they are. OK. Replace them.	6 Does it print in black? Yes, it does. OK. Press the button for 'Start Colour'.

1   *If the LEDs aren't on, check the battery.*

2   _____

3   _____

4   _____

5   _____

6   _____

3 Use verbs from the box to complete the Troubleshooting Guide.

check   check   connected   plug   plugged   press   press   shut   shuts   turns   unplug

(1) *Check* that the power cable is (2) *plugged* into the computer and a power outlet.

(3)_____ that the mouse and the keyboard are (4)_____. Unplug the cables and then (5)_____ them in again.

(6)_____ the power button on the back of the computer for a few seconds. This (7)_____ down the computer.

If you cannot (8)_____ down the computer, (9)_____ the power cable from the computer. Wait 30 seconds. Plug it back in. (10)_____. the power button. This (11)_____ the computer on.

4 Word list

NOUNS	NOUNS	VERBS	ADJECTIVES
acceleration	hovercraft	accelerate	closed
adapter	key	check	connected
airboard	laptop	connect	disconnected
battery	LED	contain	fibreglass
body	lever	control	flat
brake	modem	drive	flexible
computer	mouse	force	open
cushion	notebook computer	hold	rubber
diagram	platform	increase	**PREPOSITIONS**
disk	power button	open	above
disk drive	power outlet	press	attached **to**
display	power source	propel	below
engine	purpose	recharge	connected **to**
fan	rider	release	mounted **on**
friction wheel	router	replace	suspended **from**
front	screen	start	**PHRASES**
function	skirt	steer	pull (air) in
handlebar	speaker	stop	push (air) out
hotline	speed	support	suck (air) in)
	start button	touch	switch off
	starter motor	turn	switch on
	switch	**ADVERBS**	take out
		backwards	turn off
		downwards	turn on
		forwards	You're welcome.
		upwards	

1 Find 20 nouns that are connected to computers.

_____

_____

2 Replace the underlined words with opposites from the Word list.

1   The rider <u>presses</u> the lever.   →   _The rider releases the lever._

2   The fan <u>pushes</u> air <u>out</u>.   →   _____

3   The rider can go <u>forwards</u>.   →   _____

4   The engine is <u>above</u> the platform.   →
_____

5   The fan <u>starts</u> and the airboard goes <u>upwards</u>.   →
_____

Safety

1 Rules and warnings

1 Label the objects with these words.

safety boots   safety goggles   safety gloves   safety helmet

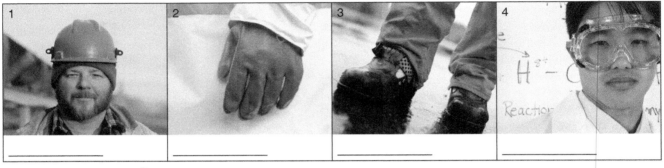

2 Use the words in the box to complete the instructions.

always   do   don't   must   mustn't   never

1   *Don't* smoke in the workshop.
2   _____ use mobile phones in the workshop.
3   You _____ wear safety goggles when you use this machine.
4   You must _____ enter the cold store if you are alone in the factory.
5   _____ not lift heavy weights by hand.
6   You _____ use this machine without the guard.
7   _____ read the manual before you service the machine.
8   _____ touch packets in the cold store without gloves.

3 Complete each sentence with a pair of verbs.

drop / break   lift / hurt   pick / burn   put / melt   touch / get
use / scratch   use / trap

1   Don't *drop* that box. You might *break* the TV inside it.
2   Don't _____ the CD on that hot surface. It could _____.
3   Don't _____ that box without a forklift truck. You might _____ your back.
4   Don't _____ a hook when you lift the car. You might _____ it.
5   Don't _____ up that hot plate. You might _____ your hand.
6   Don't _____ that wire. You could _____ an electric shock.
7   Don't _____ that machine without a guard. You could _____ your hand in it.

2 Safety hazards

1 An inspector is inspecting a factory. Write sentences from his notes.

1 liquid on floor   *There is some liquid on the floor.*

2 hole in the outside door   _____

3 no fire exit   _____

4 broken window   _____

5 cables on a workbench   _____

6 no fire extinguishers in factory   _____

7 2 machine guards missing   _____

8 some damaged warning cones   _____

2 Use phrases from the box with *might* or *could* to complete these warnings.

burn your hand fall into it get an electric shock injure your head		
start a fire trap your hair in it trip over them		

1 Mind that lighted match! (could) *You could start a fire.*

2 Mind that cable! (might) _____

3 Mind those bricks! (could) _____

4 Mind that machine! It doesn't have a guard. (might)

   _____

5 Mind the gap! (could) _____

6 Mind that low beam! (might) _____

7 Mind that circular saw! It's very hot. (could)

   _____

3 Complete the inspector's report about the hazards in a factory. Use each of the words or phrases once.

there was there were was were two no some the							

1 There *were* no fire extinguishers anywhere in the factory.

2 There was _____ food and drink on the workbenches.

3 _____ some boxes of parts on the stairs.

4 _____ guard on one of the machines was broken.

5 _____ some oil on the floor.

6 _____ of the windows were broken.

7 The fire exit _____ locked with a padlock.

8 There was _____ key for the padlock.

3 Investigations

1 ▶ **● 24** Listen to the dialogue. Complete the details on the accident report form.

About the accident	Type of accident (tick)	About the injured person
Date: _____ Time: _____ Location: _____	[ ] injured self [ ] injured somebody else [ ] slipped, tripped or fell [ ] lifted something [ ] dropped something	Name: _____ Job title: _____ Injury: _____ At work: Yes / No (circle)

2 ▶ **● 25** Listen to the questions from question 1. Complete the questions that you hear.

1 First, *where* did the accident *happen*?

2 Was _____ hurt?

3 When did it _____ _____?

4 What's the name of the _____ person?

5 What _____ he _____?

6 What's his _____?

7 Did he injure _____ _____?

8 What _____?

3 Read the newspaper story. Complete it with the words from the box.

away	between	in	in	into	into	of	on	on	on	on	out	with

---

6 FISHERMEN RESCUED

(1) *On* March 19th, there was an accident (2)_____ the North Sea. A cargo ship crashed (3)_____ the fishing boat *Marianna*. The accident happened in the North Sea (4)_____ dense fog, 300 kilometres east (5)_____ Hull. The cargo ship was (6)_____ a journey from Sweden to Portugal (7)_____ a cargo of

2000 tons of wood. The *Marianna* was (8)_____ its way back to Hull, after a four-day fishing trip. There were six fishermen on it. The captain said later: 'The anti-collision system on our boat switched (9)_____ automatically. Suddenly I saw the Swedish cargo ship. The distance (10)_____ us was only 30 metres. I tried to steer our ship (11)_____ from it. But it hit us and our boat sank. We launched our life raft, got (12)_____ it and sent (13)_____ a radio signal for help. We were in our life-raft for four hours.'

4 Word list

NOUNS	NOUNS	VERBS	PHRASAL VERBS
altitude	match	coil	look out
aviation	oven	hurt	take care
chemical	padlock	injure	take place
cloud	poison	investigate	**ADJECTIVES**
cone	prohibition	light	bare
distance	safety	lock	careful
drink	shock	mind (your head)	circular
emergency	sign	prohibit	dense
factory	site	service	mandatory
flight	surface	slip	military
food	type	touch	round
gap	warning	trap	single
gear	weight	trip	triangular
glove	**COMPOUND NOUNS**	warn	
guard		wash	
hazard	anti-collision system	wear	
high-voltage	fire exit		
hook	fire extinguisher		
investigation	flight path		
laser	mobile phone		
liquid	near miss		
machine	sea level		

1 Write adjectives to complete these phrases from the unit.

1 *dense* cloud
2 b_____ hand
3 l_____ match
4 n_____ miss
5 c_____ saw
6 e_____ shock
7 h_____-voltage

2 Complete these compound nouns from the unit.

1 *fire* extinguisher
2 s_____ boot
3 s_____ hazard
4 s_____ level
5 f_____ path
6 m_____ phone
7 b_____ site

3 Find ten nouns and compound nouns in the Word list that come from the story on page 78 of the Students' Book. Write them here.

altitude, _____

E Review

Section 1

1 Complete the description with the nouns in the box.

> acceleration   body   cushion   engine   fans
> fibreglass   levers   platform   skirt

A hovercraft moves over land and water on a
(1)_____ of air. A powerful
(2)_____ drives four large (3)_____.
They suck the air in and push the air
downwards under the rubber (4)_____. The engine is mounted on a
strong (5)_____. The (6)_____ of the hovercraft is made of foam
covered with (7)_____. Two (8)_____ control the speed of the fans
and the (9)_____ of the hovercraft.

2 Complete the dialogue with a hotline technician. Use the words in the box, some of them more than once.

> can
>
> does
>
> doesn't
>
> have
>
> haven't
>
> is
>
> I've
>
> there's

Technician: Printer Hotline. How (1)_____ I help you?

Customer: I've got a problem with my printer. It
            (2)_____ work. (3)_____ switched it on. But
            (4)_____ no light on the display.

Technician: OK. First, (5)_____ the printer connected to the AC
            adapter?

Customer: Yes, it (6)_____.

Technician: Good. And (7)_____ you connected the adapter to the
            power source?

Customer: Yes, I (8)_____.

Technician: And (9)_____ you turned the switch on?

Customer: Ah, no, I (10)_____. I'll do that now.

Technician: And (11)_____ the printer work now?

Customer: Yes, it (12)_____. Thanks.

3 Look at the flow chart for a personal watercraft. Use the chart to write a Troubleshooting Guide, using sentences with 'If'.

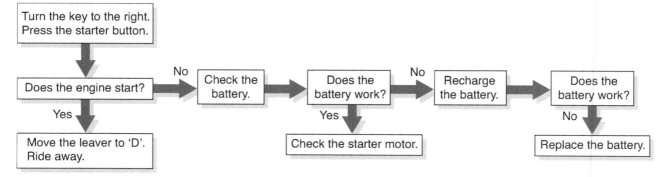

Turn the key to the right.
Press the starter button.

Does the engine start? — No → Check the battery. → Does the battery work? — No → Recharge the battery. → Does the battery work? — No → Replace the battery.

Yes ↓
Move the leaver to 'D'.
Ride away.

Yes ↓ (Does the battery work?)
Check the starter motor.

1 *Turn the key to the right. Press* _____.

2 *If the engine starts,* _____.

3 _____

4 _____

5 _____

6 _____

Section 2

1 Write these words for some safety signs in the correct order.

1 use off this after machine Turn → *Turn* _____.

2 shipyard in boots use the safety Always → _____

3 the report to Drivers must office → _____

4 the truck ride Never forklift on → _____

5 use goggles Do without machine not this safety → _____

6 supervisor reverse without You not a must → _____

2 Complete the safety report with the correct form of the verbs in brackets.

Moderna Shipyard

On 31st May, I (1)_____ (inspect) the Moderna shipyard. I (2)_____ (find) a number of safety hazards. There (3)_____ (be) some tools on the ground. There (4)_____ (be) some wire coiled outside the office. Eight of the workers (5)_____ (not have) hard hats. There (6)_____ (be) no safety signs.

In April, there (7)_____ (be) a serious incident in the shipyard. Two ships (8)_____ (be) in the shipyard. A crane (9)_____ (lift) a metal beam from one of the ships into the air. But there (10)_____ (be) no rope attached to the beam. The beam (11)_____ (come) downwards. But it (12)_____(move) in the air and (13)_____ (hit) a forklift truck. The top of the forklift truck (14)_____ (be) bent. The driver was lucky. Just before the accident, another worker (15)_____ (shout), 'Mind your head!' The driver of the forklift truck (16)_____ (see) the beam and he (17)_____ (not be) hurt.

---

3 Write questions for these answers about the incident in question 2.

1 Q: (Where / incident) *Where did the incident happen?*

A: It happened in the shipyard.

2 Q: (When / take place) _____

A: It took place in April.

3 Q: (take place / on a ship) _____

A: No. It took place near a ship, under a crane.

4 Q: (What / crane / lift) _____

A: It lifted a metal beam from the ship.

5 Q: (rope / attached / to the beam) _____

A: No, there wasn't.

6 Q: (beam / hit / worker) _____

A: No. It hit his forklift truck.

7 Q: (worker / hurt) _____

A: No, he wasn't hurt.

1 Pistons and valves

1 Complete the description of a flush toilet with words from the diagrams. Some words are used more than once, e.g. tank (4 times).

Pull the (1) *handle* down. A (2)_____ inside the tank pulls the (3)_____ up. This forces water out of the (4)_____ through the (5)_____.

When you release the (6)_____, the (7)_____ drops back into its place at the bottom of the tank. All the water flows out of the tank through the (8)_____.

There is a float ball inside the tank. It is attached to the end of the float arm. The ball makes the arm rotate vertically. The (9)_____ sinks to the bottom of the empty (10)_____. The (11)_____ rotates and opens the (12)_____. This lets water flow through the inlet pipe into the tank. The water level in the (13)_____ rises. The (14)_____ at the end of the arm rises too.

The tank fills with water. The end of the float arm now presses against the (15)_____ and closes it. This stops water from flowing into the (16)_____ through the (17)_____.

2 Tick the correct forms for the verbs.

	... it do	... it to do	... it from doing
allow		✓	
cause			
let / make			
prevent / stop			

3 Rewrite these sentences to give similar meanings. Replace the verbs in italics with the correct form of the verbs in brackets.

1 The pump *makes* the water flow along the pipes. (cause)

   The pump causes _____

2 The valves *allow* air to enter the tyres. (let)

   _____

3 The valves *don't let* air escape from the tyres. (prevent)

   _____

4 The sun *causes* the solar panel to heat the water. (make)

   _____

5 The cooling system *doesn't allow* the engine to get very hot. (stop)

   _____

6 The closed inlet valve *prevents* the water from flowing out. (not allow)

   _____

2 Switches and relays

1 Complete the description of a circuit breaker with words from the diagrams. Some words are used more than once, e.g. switch (3 times).

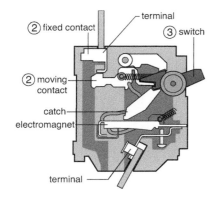

2 fixed contact
terminal
3 switch
2 moving contact
catch
electromagnet
terminal

A circuit breaker has a (1) *switch* on the outside of the box. You can turn this on or off. When the (2)_____ is up (on), electricity flows into the circuit breaker through the bottom (3)_____. It flows through the (4)_____. It then flows up to the (5)_____ and across to the (6)_____. Then the electricity flows out of the circuit breaker at the top (7)_____.

If the electrical current jumps to a dangerous level, the electromagnet pulls down a (8)_____. This pulls the (9)_____ away from the (10)_____. This breaks the circuit. At the same time, the (11)_____ drops to the 'down' position. The electricity is now shut off.

2 Read the three texts in question 3. Write the titles above the texts.

a) Emergency exit   b) Home security   c) Car security

3 Read the texts and mark the sentences 'True' (T) or 'False' (F). Correct the false parts of the sentences.

---

1 _____

This security system uses a metal ball inside a metal pipe. When the ball remains still, it touches two of the electrical contacts. This completes the electrical circuit. If the ball moves, it breaks the circuit and opens a switch. If somebody makes the car move, the system causes the horn to sound. It makes the car lights go on too. If somebody hits the car a few times, it makes the siren sound.

---

2 _____

The ExitGuard is mounted over the door handle. It has a battery-operated alarm. When somebody breaks open the ExitGuard, this causes the alarm to sound. The ExitGuard allows shops to secure their emergency exits. This stops people from using the exits to enter the shop. But it lets people leave the shop in an emergency.

---

3 _____

If you keep expensive equipment in your workshop, fit a burglar alarm. When the doors and windows of the workshop are shut, the electrical switches are closed. This allows electricity to flow around the electrical circuit. If a burglar forces open a window, this breaks the circuit. This causes the burglar alarm to sound. If your workshop is a long distance away, install the alarm buzzer inside your house. This allows you to hear the alarm when you are inside your house.

---

1   <u>Two</u> of the systems cause an alarm to sound. *F   Three*

2   The car security system works when somebody moves the car.

3   The ExitGuard works when somebody touches the door.

4   If there is a fire in a store, people can break open the ExitGuard.

5   The burglar alarm works only on the windows.

6   If the electrical circuit is broken, the burglar alarm will sound.

3 Rotors and turbines

1 Hidden word puzzle. Write the words for the pictures.

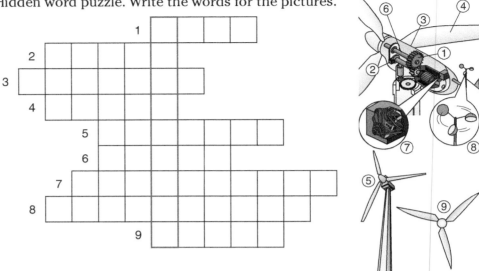

2 ▶ 🔊 **26** Write the ten words from question 1 next to their explanations. Then listen and repeat.

1   this produces electricity from the wind   *turbine*

2   this measures the speed of the wind _____

3   this switches the wind turbine on and off _____

4   this slows down the rotating shaft _____

5   two of these make the high-speed shaft rotate at 1200 rpm

    _____

6   the wind blows on three of these _____

7   this produces AC electricity _____

8   this transmits rotation to the generator _____

9   this is a strong rigid container _____

10 this consists of three blades and a hub _____

3 ▶ 🔊 **27** Listen to the interview with a company technician about a wind farm (a group of wind turbines). Circle the correct information.

1   In which state of the USA is the wind farm?
    a) New Mexico   b) Texas   c) Nebraska

2   When did the first part of the wind farm open?
    a) 2005   b) 2006   c) 2007

3   How many wind turbines are there on this wind farm?
    a) 130   b) 291   c) 421

4   Is this the largest wind farm in the world today?
    a) the largest   b) the second largest   c) the third largest

5   How many wind farms does the company have?
    a) 38   b) 48   c) 58

4 Word list

PISTONS & VALVES	SWITCHES & RELAYS	ROTORS & TURBINES	
NOUNS	**NOUNS**	**NOUNS**	**ADJECTIVES**
guard	bell	anemometer	powerful
high pressure	burglar	blade	simple
low pressure	buzzer	brake	**ADVERBS**
inlet valve	circuit	controller	automatically
outlet valve	conductor	data	**VERBS**
overflow pipe	contact	gear	download
piston	earth	generator	click
piston pump	electromagnet	high-speed shaft	**PREPOSITIONS**
shaft	magnet	housing	next to
spring	relay switch	hub	**NOUNS (NOISES)**
trigger	strip	low-speed shaft	alarm bell
VERBS	switch	rotor	beep
allow	wire	tower	buzzer
cause	**VERBS**	wind turbine	click
contract	buzz	**VERBS**	dial tone
decrease	sound	blow	door bell
expand	spring	contain	horn
explode		transmit	siren
force			
increase			
let			
prevent			
pump			
spread			

1 Find opposites in the Word list for these words.

1 allow _____   5 receive _____

2 contract _____   6 inlet _____

3 increase _____   7 high pressure _____

4 suck _____   8 low-speed _____

2 Find noises for these things.

1 the *beep* of an answerphone   5 the _____ of a telephone

2 the _____ of a car   6 the _____ of a police car

3 the _____ for a fire   7 the _____ on a door

4 the _____ of a mouse   (2 choices)

1 Data

1 Circle the names of 15 words from the text on Students' Book page 90. Some words are plurals. They go vertically from top to bottom, and sideways from left to right. No words go diagonally.

A	S	P	E	E	D	E	B	I	C	Q	O	B	F	D
E	U	D	J	D	L	M	O	T	O	R	S	U	H	K
H	S	F	M	K	A	Q	G	I	Z	D	L	C	E	G
A	P	W	A	I	X	A	N	T	E	N	N	A	S	M
Q	E	B	S	Z	O	F	Q	A	C	Y	F	M	W	U
I	N	S	T	R	U	M	E	N	T	S	Q	E	H	D
R	S	G	F	V	G	N	V	I	W	K	L	R	Z	A
D	I	A	M	E	T	E	R	U	D	H	V	A	R	F
X	O	Q	Z	W	K	Y	H	M	V	G	B	S	X	G
E	N	B	X	H	V	I	X	O	L	R	O	B	E	R
K	F	Y	K	E	L	R	K	Z	Q	O	D	F	W	H
G	L	A	S	E	R	G	U	N	G	B	Y	Y	U	R
B	W	Q	D	L	Y	A	Z	D	Z	O	W	I	G	Q
T	O	O	L	S	K	R	G	E	H	T	F	L	K	O

2 Read about the underwater robot *Jason*. Cross out the incorrect words.

Jason

Jason is an underwater science laboratory. It weighs, (1) *in/on* the surface, a little (2) *over/near* 3600 kg. It can operate (3) *in/at* a maximum depth of 6500 metres. There are some cameras and lights mounted (4) *on/over* its body. When it is (5) *about/near* the sea bed, the cameras look (6) *around/over*.

Jason has two robot arms attached (7) *on/to* the front of its frame. There are special tools (8) *from/at* the end of each robot arm. Some of the tools collect water samples. Others collect rocks (9) *over/from* the sea floor. A small pump sucks (10) *on/in* living things. An instrument measures the temperature of the water. Jason 1 started work in 1988 and worked (11) *up to/over* 2001. The new *Jason 2* has made 183 dives. It has spent (12) *near/at least* 3249 hours at the bottom of the sea.

---

3 Write questions for these answers about *Jason*. Use the information in question 2.

1 Q: What is _____?

A: It's called *Jason*.

2 Q: What _____?

A: A little over 3600 kilos.

3 Q: Where _____?
   A: They're attached to the front of the frame.

4 Q: How _____?
   A: A small pump sucks them in.

5 Q: Where _____?
   A: They're at the end of each robot arm.

6 Q: How many _____?
   A: At least 183.

2 Instructions

1 A controller is training a mobile crane driver. Match the phrases in the two boxes.

1 Press	a) the 'Start' button.
2 Press	b) forwards.
3 Release	c) to the left.
4 Push the joystick	d) the power switch. 1
5 Turn the wheel	e) the hand-brake.
6 Move forwards	f) 45° to the left.
7 Press	g) about 50 metres.
8 Rotate the arm	h) backwards.
9 Pull the joystick	i) backwards 10 metres.
10 Reverse	j) the brake pedal.

2 Make sentences with verbs and phrases from the box.

flies   goes   up and down   forwards and backwards
into space   over rocks and holes

1   A car *goes forwards and backwards.*
2   A helicopter _____ _____.
3   A motorboat _____ _____.
4   A plane _____ _____.
5   A rover _____ _____.
6   A shuttle _____ _____.
7   A truck _____ _____.

3 Re-read paragraph 1 of the text from Section 1 Data, question 2. The ship's crane is now lifting *Jason* from the sea floor. Put the verbs in brackets into the present continuous.

A: Now, lift *Jason* up to the surface. Pull in the wire.

B: It (1 not move) *isn't moving*. *Jason* (2 not come) _____ up. I think it's stuck to some rocks.

A: Move the arm of the crane to the left. Now raise the arm of the crane.

B: I (3 bring) _____ it up.

A: What (4 happen) _____ now? (5 move) _____ the craft _____?

B: Not yet. It's stuck.

A: Move the arm to the right. Bring the arm up suddenly. Now pull in the wire.

B: I (6 pull) _____ it in now. Oh no!

A: What (7 happen) _____?

B: The wire (8 come) _____ in very fast now. I think the wire is broken. And *Jason* (9 sit) _____ on the sea floor.

3 Progress

1 ▶ 🎵 28 Change these sentences, using verbs from the box. Give sentences 1–5 the opposite meaning. Then listen, check and repeat.

assemble   attach   connect   loosen   replace   take   tighten

1 Bring the large wrench from the workshop.

  1 *Take the large wrench to the workshop.*

2 Loosen the nuts on the supply pump.

  2 _____

3 Remove the pump from the supply pipe.

  3 _____

4 Dismantle the water pump.

  4 _____

5 Disconnect the valve from the pump.

  5 _____

  6 *Replace* the valve.

2 ▶ 🎵 29 The manager of an F1 racing team is talking to the engineer. Mark the jobs on the chart with a [✗] or a [✓]. Write the days/dates for finishing the jobs.

Task	Y/N?	Date for finishing
1 Remove nose cone.	✓	May 17th
2 Take photo of nose cone.		
3 Inspect fuel tank.		
4 Replace fuel pipe.		
5 Attach cables to foot pedals.		
6 Install new valves.		
7 Lubricate the gears.		
8 Test the car.		

3 Check your answers for question 2 in the Answer key. Correct them if necessary. Write sentences about the eight jobs below.

1 (they) *They've removed the nose cone.*

2 (he) *He hasn't* _____. *He'll* _____

3 (they) _____

4 (they) _____

5 (he) _____

6 (he) _____

7 (they) _____

8 (they) _____

4 Word list

NOUNS	NOUNS	VERBS	VERBS
astronaut	oxygen	analyse	remain
camera	photograph	assemble	remove
control centre	powder	check	replace
diameter	progress	collect	respond
distance	range	confirm	roll
equipment	robot	dig	support
instrument	rover	dismantle	train
laser beam	simulation	fire	**ADJECTIVES**
laser gun	surface	include	average
mass	suspension	inspect	daily
mast	system	install	mobile
million	ventilation	lubricate	scientific
obstacle	waste	operate	**ADVERBS**
		orbit	approximately
		prepare	over
		range	less than
			more than
			under

1 Find opposites in the Word list. Write them here.

1 assemble _____

2 install _____

3 leave _____

4 exclude _____

5 more than _____

6 over _____

2 Combine two nouns, one from each box. Write them below.

laser	range
robot	system
six-wheel	tank
science	beam
suspension	arm
temperature	drive
waste	laboratory

laser beam, _____

_____

Section 1

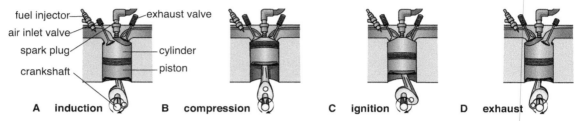

A induction   B compression   C ignition   D exhaust

1 Read about the four-stroke petrol engine. Correct the sentences, using the verbs in the box.

allow   cause   let   make   prevent   stop

A. The inlet valve opens. The round metal piston moves downwards. It stops the pressure inside the cylinder from falling.

(1) *It makes the pressure inside the cylinder fall.*

This doesn't allow a mixture of petrol and air to enter the cylinder.

(2) _____

B. The inlet valve closes. This lets the fuel mixture escape.

(3) _____

The piston moves upwards. This prevents the pressure in the cylinder from rising.

(4) _____

C. The spark plug lights the fuel and doesn't cause it to explode.

(5) _____

This forces the piston downwards on its power stroke.

D. The outlet valve opens. The piston moves upwards. This stops the burnt fuel from escaping.

(6) _____

2 Complete the description of an electricity generating station in France. Use words from the box.

blades   cables   dam   electricity   gates   generator   shaft   turbine

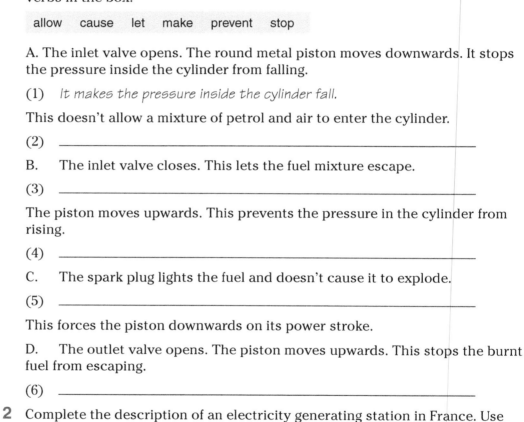

The (1) *dam* across the River Rance in France was finished in 1966. Water flows from the river into the sea through the (2)_____ in the dam. Later, it flows back into the river from the sea. The water flows past the (3)_____ of a (4)_____ and makes it rotate. A (5)_____ connects the turbine to a (6)_____. The rotation of the generator produces (7)_____. The electricity leaves the power station through high-voltage (8)_____.

Section 2

1 Write sentences about an overland rover. Use the information from the specifications chart. Change the abbreviations to words.

1 Height	202 cm	5 Wheels	steel alloy
2 Length	365 cm	6 Wheel diameter	52 cm
3 Weight	3050 kg	7 Max speed	155 kph
4 Drive	4-wheel	8 Max/Min temperature range	−40 °C min to +55 °C

1 *The rover is 202 centimetres high.*

2 *It has* _____ .

3 _____

4 _____

5 _____

6 _____

7 _____

8 _____

2 Look at the progress chart for May 4th and complete the dialogue.

Task	Yes/No?	Date for finishing
1 Collect rock samples from the rover	Y	May 4
2 Repair solar panel	N	tomorrow
3 Connect cables to solar panels	N	tomorrow
4 Replace damaged mast	Y	May 2nd
5 Assemble new robot arm	Y	May 1st
6 Replace bent wheel	N	in progress
7 Service the brake system	N	May 7th

A: Now, it's May 4th today. (1) *Have you collected* the rock samples from the rover?

B: Yes. We (2) *collected* them today.

A: Right. What about the solar panel? (3) *Have you repaired it yet?*

B: No, we (4)_____. We'll (5)_____ tomorrow.

A: Have you (6)_____ the cables to the solar panels?

B: No, not yet. (7)_____ tomorrow.

A: Right. What about the damaged mast? Have (8)_____?

B: Yes, we have. We (9)_____ May 2nd.

A: Right. What about the new robot arm? (10)_____?

B: Yes, we (11)_____ May 1st.

A: Have you (12)_____ the bent wheel yet?

B: No, we're still (13)_____ that.

A: What about the brake system? (14)_____?

B: No, we haven't. We (15)_____ May 7th.

Audioscript

Unit 1 Check-up

> 🔊 **02**

I'm Alex Greyson, that's G–R–E–Y–S–O–N.
My phone number is oh oh four four, oh one nine six two, eight oh four nine two seven.
My email address is alex G forty at rossi dot co dot uk, that's A–L–E–X–G forty at rossi dot co dot uk.

> 🔊 **03**

Receptionist:	Welcome, Madam. Could you give me your surname, please?
Guest:	Yes, it's Johnstone. J–O–H–N–S–T–O–N–E.
Receptionist:	And your first name, Madam?
Guest:	Anne, with an E. So that's A–double N–E.
Receptionist:	And your company name, Madam?
Guest:	It's Weyco.
Receptionist:	How do you spell that?
Guest:	W–E–Y–C–O.
Receptionist:	Thank you. And your email address?
Guest:	It's aj309 at plas.com. That's A–J–three–oh–nine at plas.com. That's P–L–A–S dot com.
Receptionist:	Thank you. I've got that.

> 🔊 **04**

Mr Martin:	Has this car done a lot of kilometres?
Salesman:	It has done, er … one hundred and twenty thousand kilometres.
Mr Martin:	One hundred and twenty thousand! Oh! That's a lot.
Salesman:	It's a very nice car. I'll open the door for you. There!
Mr Martin:	Mmm. What's that inside the car?
Salesman:	That shows the temperature in the engine. Normally, it's ninety degrees Celsius.
Mr Martin:	What's that on the right?
Salesman:	That's for the petrol tank.
Mr Martin:	How big is the tank?
Salesman:	It holds fifty-five litres.
Mr Martin:	That's good.
Salesman:	And the engine goes up to six thousand rpm.
Mr Martin:	Six thousand rpm? That's fast.
Salesman:	Yes. It can go at one hundred and eighty-five kilometres per hour.
Mr Martin:	One hundred and eighty-five! Now that is fast! How much is it?
Salesman:	The price is fifteen thousand nine hundred and fifty euros.
Mr Martin:	Is that all? Then I'll buy it!

Unit 2 Parts (1)

> 🔊 **05**

Message 1:	My name is Vladyslaw, that's V–L–A–D–Y–S–L–A–W Szczecin, that's spelt S–Z–C–Z–E–C–I–N. And my phone number is 00 48 920 4916.
Message 2:	My name is Abdel, that's A–B–D–E–L, Mohammed, that's M–O–H–A–double M–E–D, Mabrouk, that's M–A–B–R–O–U–K. My phone number is 00 20 537 1498.

> 🔊 **06**

Message 1:	Hello, I'm calling on the fourteenth of February and it's eleven forty-five now. Could you call me back, please? I need some parts for my car. My name is Jon, that's J–O–N, Bradleigh, that's B–R–A–D–L–E–I–G–H. And my phone number is 01962 4377. Thank you. Bye.
Message 2:	Hello, I'm calling at two thirty. The date today is er ehm January the 30th. I need some parts for my car, so could you call me back, please? My name is Olof, that's O–L–O–F, Hansson, that's H–A–N–double S–O–N. My phone number is 01720 3399. Thanks.

> 🔊 **07**

Salesperson:	Hello. Customer Sales. Can I help you?
Customer:	Yes, I need some skateboard things.
Salesperson:	What do you need?
Customer:	I need some helmets.
Salesperson:	How many do you need?
Customer:	I need four large helmets.
Salesperson:	What colour?
Customer:	Red.
Salesperson:	So that's four large red helmets.
Customer:	That's right. And I need to order some pads.
Salesperson:	How many do you need?
Customer:	I need six pads.
Salesperson:	Large, medium or small?
Customer:	Small, please.
Salesperson:	And what colour?
Customer:	Blue.
Salesperson:	So that's six small blue pads. What's your name please?
Customer:	Webster, that's W–E–B–S–T–E–R.
Salesperson:	And your initials?
Customer:	My initial is S.
Salesperson:	And your address, please?

Customer:	14 Selly Park, that's two words, S–E–double L–Y, Park, that's P–A–R–K, Birmingham. That's B–I–R–M–I–N–G–H–A–M.
Salesperson:	And your postcode?
Customer:	BM29 8JE.
Salesperson:	And what's your phone number?
Customer:	0121 414 0433.
Salesperson:	OK, I've got that.

Unit 3 Parts (2)

▶ 💿 08

Driver:	I have some boxes of speakers here. Where do you want them?
Manager:	Put them at the bottom, on the right.
Driver:	Where do the scanners go?
Manager:	They go … on the middle shelf, on the right.
Driver:	Where do you want the adapters?
Manager:	Adapters, er ehm, at the top, on the left.
Driver:	Mouse pads?
Manager:	What?
Driver:	Where do the mouse pads go?
Manager:	Mouse pads go on the bottom shelf, in the middle.
Driver:	Where do you want the printers?
Manager:	The printers go on the top shelf, on the right.
Driver:	Where do the headphones go?
Manager:	The headphones go on the top shelf, in the centre.
Driver:	Where do I put the amplifiers?
Manager:	Put those on the middle shelf, on the left.
Driver:	DVD players? Where do they go?
Manager:	They go at the bottom, on the left.
Driver:	Keyboards? Where do you want those?
Manager:	Keyboards go … middle shelf, in the centre. Any more?
Driver:	No, that's all.

▶ 💿 09

A:	There are lots of things here. Where do I put the multi-tool?
B:	Put the multi-tool above the hammer.
A:	Above the hammer. OK. Where do I put the pliers?
B:	Put those to the right of the dynamo.
A:	To the right of the dynamo. OK. Where does the radio go?
B:	The radio goes above the dynamo.
A:	OK. Where does the wrench go?
B:	The wrench goes … below the dynamo.
A:	Where do I put the batteries?
B:	Put those to the left of the DVD drive.
A:	OK. Where do I put the torch?
B:	Put it to the right of the DVD drive.
A:	To the right of the DVD drive, so above the computer.
B:	That's good! Any more things?
A:	Yes, scissors.
B:	Put the scissors to the right of the wrench.
A:	That's all.

Unit 4 Movement

▶ 💿 10

1 thirty kilometres per hour
2 five hundred revolutions per minute
3 fifteen metres per second
4 sixty-five miles per hour
5 eight kilometres per second

▶ 💿 11

1 Sound travels at 300 metres per second.
2 The engine of a Formula 1 car turns at about nineteen thousand revolutions per minute.
3 The moon truck Apollo 16 Rover travels at 18 kilometres per hour.
4 A solar-powered car can travel at 83 miles per hour.
5 A person on skis can go downhill at two hundred and forty-eight kilometres per hour.
6 A person on a snowboard can go downhill at two hundred and one kilometres per hour.
7 The maximum speed of a train in France is five hundred and seventy-four kilometres per hour.
8 The fastest sailing ship sails at eighty-six kilometres per hour.
9 A Blackbird jet flies at one thousand nine hundred and seventy-nine miles per hour.

▶ 💿 12

A:	This is a list of the things in the box.
B:	Good!
A:	So, what's in the box? I can tick the things off on this list.
B:	Here's the truck. Look! It's very nice.
A:	What else?
B:	One antenna.
A:	For the truck or the transmitter?
B:	One for the transmitter, and … here we are … one on the truck.
A:	Batteries?
B:	One nine-volt battery.
A:	Only one? We need two.
B:	There's only one in the box.
A:	Oh dear. Do you have the instruction manual?
B:	No, it's not in the box.
A:	Oh no! Where is the instruction manual? We need it!
B:	Ah! I can see it. It's in your hand!

Unit 5 Flow

▶ 💿 13

1 If the river is high, and the workshop is open, the current flows from the generator into the workshop.
2 If the river is high, and the workshop is closed, the current flows from the generator into the batteries.
3 If the river is low, and the workshop is open, the current flows from the batteries into the workshop.
4 If the river is low, and the workshop is closed, the current does not flow.
5 If the batteries are full, the current does not flow from the generator into the batteries.

6 If the batteries are empty, the current does not flow from the batteries into the workshop.

▶ 🔊 14

Customer:	I need some things for a solar power system. First, I need some solar panels.
Shopkeeper:	How many do you need?
Customer:	I need four sixty watt panels.
Shopkeeper:	Right. Anything else?
Customer:	Yes, I need a controller.
Shopkeeper:	How many amps?
Customer:	One five amp controller.
Shopkeeper:	Right.
Customer:	And I need some batteries.
Shopkeeper:	How many do you need?
Customer:	I need four twelve volt one hundred ampere hour batteries.
Shopkeeper:	Can you say that again?
Customer:	Yes, four batteries, twelve volt, one hundred ampere hours.
Shopkeeper:	Right, that's clear.
Customer:	And I need some lamps.
Shopkeeper:	How many?
Customer:	I need six twelve volt eight watt lamps.
Shopkeeper:	Six or sixteen lamps?
Customer:	Six lamps, please. And I need some cable.
Shopkeeper:	How many metres of cable do you want?
Customer:	I need twelve metres.
Shopkeeper:	What size?
Customer:	Six millimetre, fifty-three amps.
Shopkeeper:	Right.

Unit 6 Materials

▶ 🔊 15

Sales clerk:	And what equipment do you want to order?
Customer:	I need a backpack.
Sales clerk:	How many backpacks do you want?
Customer:	Only one.
Sales clerk:	And do you have the product number?
Customer:	Yes, it's 19 forward slash one two four.
Sales clerk:	One nine forward slash one two four. Now, we do the backpack in orange, red, green or blue. Which colour do you want?
Customer:	Er, ehm, green, please.
Sales clerk:	Now, the backpack comes in four different sizes, extra-large, large, medium or small. Which size do you want?
Customer:	Large, please.
Sales clerk:	OK. Next the material. You can have it in nylon or polyester.
Customer:	Polyester, please. I don't want a nylon one.
Sales clerk:	And the price is … a hundred and twenty-five dollars. Or do you want the price in euros?
Customer:	No, dollars is fine. So that's a hundred and twenty-five dollars, then.

▶ 🔊 16

1
A:	John. Can you give me your email address again, please?
B:	OK. It's J Clarke with an E, so that's J–C–L–A–R–K–E, at i-way, that's I hyphen W–A–Y dot co dot U–K.
A:	Can I check that? J–C–L–A–R–K–E, at i-way, that's I hyphen W–A–Y dot co dot U–K.
B:	Correct.

2
A:	Alex. Can I check your email address?
B:	My email address is now Alex 2, that's A–L–E–X then number 2, at anti dash G–M dot org.
A:	Org?
B:	O–R–G.
A:	Can I read it back to you? Alex 2, that's A–L–E–X then number 2, at anti dash G–M dot org.
B:	That's right.

3
A:	Sandrine, can I check your email address?
B:	Yes. It's S underscore Hagen, that's H–A–G–E–N, at Renault dot FR.
A:	How do you spell 'Renault'?
B:	R–E–N–A–U–L–T.
A:	So that's S underscore Hagen, that's H–A–G–E–N, at Renault dot F–R. F–R not F–R–A?
B:	Yes. That's right.

▶ 🔊 17

1
A:	Here's a good website for news.
B:	OK. What is it?
A:	B–B–C dot co dot U–K forward slash newsline.
B:	Is newsline one word?
A:	Yes. N–E–W–S–L–I–N–E.

2
A:	Do you know a good website for live radio?
B:	Yes. Try this one. It's live dash radio dot net.
A:	Live dash radio dot net. Thanks.

3
A:	Do you know the website for the toy company?
B:	Yes. It's sci-toys, that's S–C–I hyphen toys dot com forward slash prod forward slash 51.
A:	Is prod P–R–O–D?
B:	Yes.
A:	So that's S–C–I hyphen toys dot com forward slash P–R–O–D forward slash 51.
B:	Correct.

Unit 7 Specifications

▶ 🔊 18

Shopkeeper:	Hello. Can I help you?
Customer:	Yes, I'm repairing my workshop and I'm looking at your order form. First, I need some paint.
Shopkeeper:	How much paint do you need?
Customer:	Oh, about forty litres.
Shopkeeper:	What colour paint do you need?
Customer:	Green.
Shopkeeper:	And what size tin do you need? We have five-litre tins and ten-litre tins.
Customer:	I need four ten-litre tins, please.
Shopkeeper:	Four ten-litre tins. Do you have the product number on the order form?
Customer:	Yes, it's P one seven six G–R.
Shopkeeper:	OK. Anything else?

Customer:	I need some cement.
Shopkeeper:	How much cement do you need? We sell it in 10-kilo bags and 20-kilo bags. How many bags do you need?
Customer:	I need five 20-kilo bags, please.
Shopkeeper:	Five 20-kilo bags. What colour? White or grey?
Customer:	White, please.
Shopkeeper:	What's the product number, please?
Customer:	It's C zero one one six W.
Shopkeeper:	OK.
Customer:	Now, do you have any screws?
Shopkeeper:	Yes. What size do you need?
Customer:	24 mil.
Shopkeeper:	How many screws do you need?
Customer:	About four hundred.
Shopkeeper:	We sell them in packets of fifty or one hundred.
Customer:	So I need four packets of one hundred.
Shopkeeper:	And the product number, please?
Customer:	S double zero nine four one.
Shopkeeper:	OK. Do you need any nails?
Customer:	No. I don't need any nails, thanks.

▶ 🔊 19

1 How much paint do you need?
2 What colour paint do you need?
3 What size tin do you need?
4 How much cement do you need?
5 How many bags do you need?
6 Do you have any screws?
7 How many screws do you need?
8 Do you need any nails?

Unit 8 Reporting

▶ 🔊 20

1 They have bent the router antenna.
2 The user manual is torn.
3 Someone has broken the camera.
4 The body of the radio is cracked.
5 The speakers are damaged.
6 Someone has cut the power cable.
7 The lenses of the goggles are scratched.
8 I have burnt my overalls.
9 They have dented the car door.

▶ 🔊 21

Part 1

Customer Services:	Customer Services. Please can I have your order number?
Customer:	Yes, it's PC zero eight. Forward slash one zero two zero. Forward slash double zero one seven.
Customer Services:	OK. I've got that. Can I check your details? You're Mr Bert Sandle?
Customer:	Yes, but you spelt my name wrong. It's B–U–R–T and then S–A–N–D–E double L.
Customer Services:	B–U–R–T, S–A–N–D–E double L. I'm sorry about that. And can I
	check your address, Mr Sandell? Is it 14 Hayford Road, Catford, London?
Customer:	Yes, but you've got the wrong postcode. My postcode is S–E ten, four Q–Y.
Customer Services:	S–E ten, four Q–Y. And your telephone number?
Customer:	Oh two oh eight, four double one, four double oh nine.
Customer Services:	Good, I've got that. And your email address?
Customer:	It's bsandell87@pdq.com.
Customer Services:	Can you repeat that, please?
Customer:	Yes, it's B–S–A–N–D–E double L eight seven at P–D–Q dot com.
Customer Services:	At P–D–Q dot com. OK, I've got that.

Part 2

Customer Services:	Now, you bought a computer from us. How can I help you?
Customer:	I think somebody dropped the box. Some things are damaged and some things are missing.
Customer Services:	Oh, I'm sorry to hear that. What's missing?
Customer:	The mouse is missing.
Customer Services:	Mouse missing. Anything else?
Customer:	You know the antenna on the router? Well, it's bent.
Customer Services:	Antenna bent. Is there any more damage?
Customer:	Yes, the computer screen is scratched.
Customer Services:	OK. Computer screen scratched.
Customer:	And the keyboard is broken.
Customer Services:	Broken?
Customer:	Yes, it's broken.
Customer Services:	Keyboard broken. Anything else?
Customer:	There's no plug on the power cable.
Customer Services:	No plug on cable. Is that all?
Customer:	There's some more damage: the left-hand speaker is damaged.
Customer Services:	Left-hand speaker damaged.
Customer:	And the right-hand speaker has a hole in the front.
Customer Services:	Hole in the front of right-hand speaker. Is that all?
Customer:	The user manual is missing.
Customer Services:	No user manual.
Customer:	That's all.
Customer Services:	Oh dear. I'm very sorry about this. Please put everything back in the box. We'll collect it from your house and we'll bring you a new computer.
Customer:	That's good.
Customer Services:	Thank you for calling, Mr Sandell.

Unit 9 Troubleshooting

 22

Dialogue 1

Service technician:	Hello. How can I help you?
Customer:	My computer isn't working.
Service technician:	OK. Is the display open or closed?
Customer:	It's open.
Service technician:	Is the mouse connected?
Customer:	Yes, it is.
Service technician:	And is the disk drive connected?
Customer:	Yes, it is.
Service technician:	Is the adapter connected?
Customer:	No, it isn't.
Service technician:	And is the power switch up or down?
Customer:	It's up.

Dialogue 2

Service technician:	Hello. How can I help you?
Customer:	My computer isn't working.
Service technician:	OK. First of all, is the display open or closed?
Customer:	It's open.
Service technician:	And is the adapter connected?
Customer:	Yes, it is.
Service technician:	Is the power switch up or down?
Customer:	It's down.
Service technician:	And is the mouse connected?
Customer:	Yes, it is.
Service technician:	Is the speaker connected?
Customer:	No, it isn't connected.

Dialogue 3

Service technician:	Hello. What can I do for you?
Customer:	My computer isn't working.
Service technician:	OK. Is the display open or closed?
Customer:	It's open.
Service technician:	Now look at the power switch. Is it up or down?
Customer:	It's down.
Service technician:	Is the speaker connected?
Customer:	No, it's disconnected.
Service technician:	Ah. And is the disk drive connected?
Customer:	Yes, it's connected.
Service technician:	Is the mouse connected?
Customer:	It's disconnected.
Service technician:	Ah. I think I've found the problem.

 23

Dialogue 1

Service technician:	Does the computer start?
Customer:	No, it doesn't.
Service technician:	Right. Press the power button again.

Dialogue 2

Service technician:	Is the power switch down?
Customer:	No, it isn't.

Service technician:	OK. Press it down.

Dialogue 3

Service technician:	Are the loudspeakers connected?
Customer:	No, they aren't.
Service technician:	OK. Connect them.

Dialogue 4

Service technician:	Is the adapter connected?
Customer:	Yes, it is.
Service technician:	Good.

Dialogue 5

Service technician:	Do the loudspeakers work?
Customer:	No, they don't.
Service technician:	OK. Connect them and try again.

Dialogue 6

Service technician:	Are the two LED lights on?
Customer:	Yes, they are.
Service technician:	Good.

Dialogue 7

Service technician:	Does the computer start?
Customer:	Yes, it does.
Service technician:	Good.

Dialogue 8

Service technician:	Do the loudspeakers work now?
Customer:	Yes, they do.
Service technician:	Good.

Unit 10 Safety

 24

Worker:	There's been an accident!
Supervisor:	Oh no! Was anybody hurt?
Worker:	Yes, Peter the Storeman.
Supervisor:	Where is he now?
Worker:	He's gone to hospital.
Supervisor:	OK. I must fill in this form. First, where did the accident happen?
Worker:	In Number 6 workshop.
Supervisor:	In Number 6 workshop. And when did it take place?
Worker:	At half-past three this afternoon.
Supervisor:	So, three-thirty pm. And today is …
Worker:	March the twenty-ninth.
Supervisor:	Thanks. So, what's the name of the injured person?
Worker:	Peter Graski. That's G–R–A–S–K–I.
Supervisor:	OK. What does he do? What's his job?
Worker:	He's the Storeman.
Supervisor:	S–T–O–R–E–M–A–N. Did he injure anybody else?
Worker:	No, only himself.
Supervisor:	So nobody else. What exactly happened?
Worker:	He lifted a bar of steel alone. And he hurt his back. So he dropped the bar on his boot. His foot is injured.
Supervisor:	So, he didn't slip and he didn't trip and he didn't fall, but he lifted something and he dropped something. And you say his back is injured.

Worker:	Yes, his back and his foot.
Supervisor:	And you say he's not at work now.
Worker:	Correct. He's gone to hospital.

25

1 First, where did the accident happen?
2 Was anybody hurt?
3 When did it take place?
4 What's the name of the injured person?
5 What does he do?
6 What's his job?
7 Did he injure anybody else?
8 What happened?

Unit 11 Cause and Effect

26

1 turbine
2 anemometer
3 controller
4 brake
5 gear
6 blade
7 generator
8 shaft
9 housing
10 rotor

27

Interviewer:	So where have you opened this big wind farm?
Company technician:	In Texas.
Interviewer:	Sorry?
Company technician:	Texas. Here, look at the map.
Interviewer:	When did it open?
Company technician:	The first part opened in two thousand and five. The second part opened in two thousand and six. And the third and last part opened in two thousand and seven.
Interviewer:	I see. How many wind turbines are there on this wind farm?
Company technician:	Let me see. There are two hundred and ninety-one, plus one hundred and thirty. That makes a total of four hundred and twenty-one.
Interviewer:	So many wind turbines! Is this the biggest wind farm in the world?
Company technician:	Right now, it is the biggest in the world. Maybe next year, or the year after, it'll be the second biggest. Or the third biggest. That's all in the future.
Interviewer:	Do you have any other wind farms?
Company technician:	Of course. We have some other wind farms in different states of the USA.
Interviewer:	How many?

Company technician:	Right now, we have a total of forty-eight wind farms.
Interviewer:	That's a lot of wind turbines!
Company technician:	You're right! And they make electricity for all our customers.

Unit 12 Checking and confirming

28

Left-hand column, from the top to the bottom
1 Bring the large wrench from the workshop.
2 Loosen the nuts on the supply pump.
3 Remove the pump from the supply pipe.
4 Dismantle the water pump.
5 Disconnect the valve from the pump.
6 Replace the valve.

Right-hand column, from the bottom to the top
5 Connect the valve to the pump.
4 Assemble the water pump.
3 Attach the pump to the supply pipe.
2 Tighten the nuts on the supply pipe.
1 Take the large wrench to the workshop.

29

Manager:	Hello. I'm checking progress on the repairs to our Formula One car.
Engineer:	One moment. I'll get the progress chart. OK.
Manager:	It's May the seventeenth today. Have you removed the damaged nose cone yet?
Engineer:	Yes, we have.
Manager:	Good. So I can put a tick against that job. And have you taken a photo of the nose cone?
Engineer:	No, not yet.
Manager:	When will you do that?
Engineer:	I'll do it today, May the seventeenth.
Manager:	OK. Now, the next thing on my list. Have you inspected the fuel tank yet?
Engineer:	Yes, we have. It was damaged.
Manager:	So, you haven't replaced the fuel pipes yet.
Engineer.	Correct. We haven't.
Manager:	When will you do that job?
Engineer:	We'll do that on May the nineteenth.
Manager:	May the nineteenth. OK. Now, the next thing on my list. Have you attached the cables to the foot pedals?
Engineer:	Yes, I've finished that job.
Manager:	And have you installed the new valves on the engine yet?
Engineer:	Yes, I've done that too.
Manager:	Now. Lubricating the gears. Have you done that job yet?
Engineer:	No. We'll do that on May the twentieth.
Manager:	And you need to test the car. When will you do that?
Engineer:	If everything is OK, we'll test the car on May the twenty-second.
Manager:	Good! I've noted all that information. Thanks.

Answer key

1 Check-up

1 Basics

1
1. I'm, is
2. Where, What
3. Are, I'm, What's

2
1. Stand up.
2. Write your name.
3. Turn right.
4. Close your book.
5. Sit down.
6. Raise your hand.
7. Come in.

3

Tools	Electricals	Fixings
chisel	adapter	bolts
saw	antenna	nuts
screwdriver	cable	screws
spanner	plug	washers

2 Letters and numbers

1
Rossi Air
Alex Greyson
Aerospace Technician
Tel: (0044) (0)1962 804927
Email: alexg40@rossi.co.uk

2
Surname: Johnstone
First name: Anne
Company: Weyco
Email address: aj309@plas.com

3
1. gallon
2. euro
3. kilogram
4. amp
5. inch
6. foot
7. kilometre
8. angle/degree
9. gram
10. Celsius
11. positive
12. metre
13. kilowatt
14. volt
15. kilometres per hour
16. revolutions per minute
17. watt
18. litre
19. pound
20. negative

4
1. Kilometres: 120 000 km
2. Engine temperature: 90 °Celsius
3. Petrol tank: 55 litres
4. Engine speed: up to 6000 rpm
5. Top speed: 185 kph
6. Price: 15 950 euros

3 Dates and times

1
4th	fourth	5th	fifth
12th	twelfth	29th	twenty-ninth
23rd	twenty-third	8th	eighth
7th	seventh	31st	thirty-first
30th	thirtieth	6th	sixth
22nd	twenty-second	20th	twentieth

2
1. January the thirty-first is a Friday, so February the eighth is a Saturday.
2. March the twenty-ninth is a Wednesday, so April the second is a Sunday.
3. May the twenty-ninth is a Tuesday, so June the third is a Sunday.
4. July the thirtieth is a Thursday, so August the fourth is a Tuesday.
5. September the twenty-eighth is a Monday, so October the seventh is a Wednesday.
6. November the twenty-seventh is a Thursday, so December the sixth is a Saturday.

3
A: When's the meeting?
B: It's on Monday.
A: Is that Monday 12th?
B: Yes. That's right.
A: Do you know what time?
B: It's at 10 o'clock.
A: OK. See you then. Bye.
B: Bye.

4 Word list

Sample answers
1. 425 grams   22 kilograms
2. 23 °Celsius
3. 23 metres   6 foot/feet   12 inches
4. 79 kilometres
5. 110 kilometres per hour
6. 3500 revolutions per minute
7. 45 litres
8. 6000 euros
9. Two hundred and twenty-five volts

2 Parts (1)

1 Naming

1
1. That's the wheel of a racing car.
2. That's the axle of a mountain bike.
3. That's the nose of a plane.
4. That's the number plate of a motorbike.
5. That's the tail of a rocket.
6. That's the deck of a boat.

2
1. That isn't a hammer. That's a screwdriver.
2. Those aren't screws. Those are nails.
3. This isn't a chisel. This is a spanner.
4. These aren't washers. These are nuts.
5. This isn't a nail. This is a staple.
6. These aren't nuts. These are bolts.
7. That isn't a staple. That's a screw.
8. Those aren't nuts. Those are washers.

2 Assembling

1
1. Raise the car with the jack.
2. Loosen all the nuts with the box spanner.

3 Take off all the nuts.
4 Take the wheel off the axle.
5 Put the spare wheel on the axle.
6 Put on all the nuts.
7 Tighten all the nuts with the box spanner.
8 Lower the car.

2 Shopkeeper: Hello.
   Customer: Hello. I need some nails, please.
   Shopkeeper: Some nails. What size do you need?
   Customer: 30 mil, please.
   Shopkeeper: 30 mil. How many nails do you need?
   Customer: I need 80, please.

3 Ordering

1 1 Name: Vladyslaw Szczecin
      Phone number: 00 48 920 4916

   2 Name: Abdel Mohammed Mabrouk
      Phone number: 00 20 537 1498

2 1   2

   Date: 14th February   Date: January 30th
   Time: 11.45   Time: 2.30
   Caller: Jon Bradleigh   Caller: Olof Hansson
   Phone number: Phone number:
         01962 4377   01720 3399

3 Surname: Webster, S
   Address: 14 Selly Park, Birmingham
   Postal code: B29
   Tel: 0121 414 0433
   Order: four large red helmets, six small blue
               pads

4 Word list

1 wheel, hammer, spanner, assemble, loosen, pull,
   small, yellow

2 Tools: hammer, lever, screwdriver, spanner

   Things: bolt, nail, nut, screw, staple, washer

3 **Before skateboarding**
   Put on the helmet.
   Push it down onto your head.
   Tighten the helmet strap.
   Put on the pads.
   Tighten the pads.

   After skateboarding
   Loosen the pads and take them off.
   Loosen the helmet strap and take off the helmet.

Review Unit A

Section 1

1 1 Are, I'm, That's
   2 do, I'm
   3 Is, he's

2 1 February 1st, 2011
   2 March 9th, 2011
   3 January 22nd, 2011
   4 November 12th, 2011
   5 July 8th, 2011
   6 October 9th, 2011

3 1 Monday, May the first
   2 Thursday, May the fourth
   3 Sunday, May the seventh
   4 Wednesday, May the tenth
   5 Saturday, May the thirteenth
   6 Tuesday, May the sixteenth
   7 Friday, May the nineteenth
   8 Monday, May the twenty-second

Section 2

1 1 bolts   4 nuts   7 skateboards
   2 washers   5 nails
   3 screws   6 axles

2 A: What's this tool called?
   B: It's a hammer.
   A: Is it for screws?
   B: No. It's for nails.
   A: What's this tool called?
   B: It's a screwdriver.
   A: Is it for nails?
   B: No. It's for screws.

3 A: Hello. I need to order some business cards.
   B: How many do you need?
   A: 200, please.
   B: What size cards do you need?
   A: 85 millimetres by 55 millimetres.
   B: What's your name?
   A: Stevens, with a V. Initials HC.
   B: What's your address and postal code?
   A: 14 Hayfield Road, Bristol. BR7 4JK
   B: What's your phone number?
   A: 0117 893462.
   B: What's your email address?
   A: It's harry.stevens@ojs.com
   B: When do you want them?
   A: Friday, please.

3 Parts (2)

1 Tools

1 1 scissors   7 pliers
   2 screw   8 chisel
   3 ruler   9 cover
   4 hammer   10 can opener
   5 wrench   11 spanner
   6 blade   12 screwdriver

2 1 screwdriver   4 spanner
   2 hammer   5 pair of pliers
   3 pair of scissors 6 saw

3 1 Does, doesn't, Does, does, have, has
   2 Do, don't, Do, do, have, has

2 Functions

1 1 generator   6 electricity
   2 compass   7 temperature
   3 battery   8 handle
   4 adapter   9 thermometer
   5 antenna   10 dynamo

2
1 turn
2 turns
3 charges
4 shine
5 listen
6 produces
7 charge

3 Locations

1
8 adapters	5 headphones	9 printers
6 amplifiers	2 keyboards	4 scanners
3 DVD players	7 mouse pads	1 speakers

The products are in alphabetical order from top to bottom and from left to right.

2
batteries 1	pliers 9
torch 3	wrench 11
radio 5	scissors 12
multi-tool 7	

4 Word list

1 Chisels cut wood.
2 Hammers drive in nails.
3 Pliers grip wire.
4 Rulers measure everything.
5 Saws cut metal.
6 Scissors cut paper.
7 Screwdrivers loosen screws.
8 Wrenches tighten nuts.

4 Movement

1 Directions

1 A vertical take-off (Picture 2)
A short take-off (Picture 1)
vertically up (C), horizontal (A, D), diagonally up (B)

2
1 straight up	4 up and down
2 forwards	5 sideways
3 to the right	6 straight down

3
1 pivots	6 rotate
2 directions	7 hip
3 ankle	8 angles
4 degrees	9 knee
5 move	10 sideways

2 Instructions

1
1 thirty kilometres per hour
2 five hundred revolutions per minute
3 fifteen metres per second
4 sixty-five miles per hour
5 eight kilometres per second

2
1 300 m/s	4 83 mph	7 574 kph
2 19 000 rpm	5 248 kph	8 86 kph
3 18 kph	6 201 kph	9 1979 mph

3 Instruction manual (✓)
Transmitter (✓)
Truck (✓)
Antenna for transmitter (✓)
Antenna for truck (✓)
2 9 V batteries (only one)

4
1 sends
2 receives
3 use
4 control
5 turns
6 Press
7 moves

3 Actions

1
1 G	3 B	5 C	7 D
2 H	4 A	6 F	8 E

2
1 When you pull the gear lever to 'R', the car reverses.
2 When you pull the gear lever to 'D', the car moves forwards.
3 When you press the accelerator, the car goes faster.
4 When you press the brake pedal a little, the car goes slower.
5 When you turn the steering wheel to the right, the car turns right.
6 When you turn the steering wheel to the left, the car turns left.
7 When you press the brake pedal, the car stops.

3
C Drive forwards slowly. Stop.
D Reverse and turn the steering wheel to the left.
B Reverse a little more and turn the steering wheel to the right. Stop.
A Drive forwards a little and turn the steering wheel to the left.

4 Word list

1 accelerator, antenna (for the radio), brake, handle (for a door), lever, parking brake, pedal, steering wheel, switch (for the lights)

2 accelerate / slow down
ascend / descend
pull / push
forwards / backwards
up / down
to the left / to the right

3 Helicopters can accelerate, ascend, descend, reverse, rotate, slow down, turn round.

Review Unit B

Section 1

1
1 The screen is in the centre. (✓)
2 The keyboard is in the centre, below the screen.
3 The TV is to the left of the screen.
4 The VCR is on the left, below the TV. (✓)
5 Speaker 1 is on the left.
6 Speaker 2 is on the right.
7 The mouse is at the bottom, to the right of the keyboard.
8 The DVD drive is above the mouse, to the right of the screen.

2

football	planes	the news
bikes	science	cars
boats	skateboards	space

1 Football is at the top, on the left.
2 Planes are at the top, in the centre.
3 The news is at the top, on the right.
4 Bikes are on the middle line, on the left.
5 Science is on the middle line, in the centre.
6 Cars are on the middle line, on the right.
7 Boats are at the bottom, on the left.
8 Skateboards are at the bottom, in the centre.
9 Space is at the bottom, on the right.

3 1 battery, hammer, spanner, wrench
  2 a pair of overalls, a pair of pincers, a pair of pliers, a pair of scissors

Section 2

1 1 D: forwards and backwards
  2 C: rotate
  3 A: descend, diagonal or horizontal
  4 B: up and down

2 1 Can you find the user manual?
    No, I can't find it.
  2 How does the truck work?
    It receives signals from the transmitter.
  3 Where do I put the battery?
    You put it in the transmitter.
  4 Where does the antenna go?
    It goes on top of the truck.
  5 How do I steer the truck?
    You press one of the control buttons.
  6 Are there two batteries in the box?
    No, there is only one.
  7 Do we need a second battery?
    Yes, we need it for the truck.

3 D Start the engine. Tie the rope on the <u>left</u> of the boat to Point A.
  B Turn the steering wheel to the left. Push the engine lever forwards; this moves the boat slowly <u>forwards</u> and to the <u>left</u>.
  C Pull the engine lever to the <u>centre</u> position. Loosen the rope. Take off the rope from Point A.
  A Turn the steering wheel to the <u>centre</u> position. Pull the lever <u>backwards</u>; this puts the engine into reverse. Reverse slowly.

5 Flow

1 Heating system

1 | | | |
|---|---|---|
| sink / rise | out of / into | enter / leave |
| above / below | cold / hot | outlet / inlet |
| bottom / top | cool / heat | push / pull |

2 1 A fridge cools water.
  2 Cold water sinks to the bottom of a water tank.
  3 The outlet pipe for hot water is above the pump.
  4 Water leaves the tank through the outlet pipe.
  5 Pull the shower head out of the pipe.

3 1 above   5 out of   9 leaves
  2 below   6 flows   10 to
  3 pushes 7 through
  4 into   8 rises

2 Electrical circuit

1 1 lamp   5 electrical current
  2 solar panel   6 controller
  3 battery   7 cable
  4 switch

2 1 If the river is high, and the workshop is open, the current flows from the generator into the workshop.
  2 If the river is high, and the workshop is closed, the current flows from the generator into the batteries.
  3 If the river is low, and the workshop is open, the current flows from the batteries into the workshop.
  4 If the river is low, and the workshop is closed, the current does not flow.
  5 If the batteries are full, the current does not flow from the generator into the batteries.
  6 If the batteries are empty, the current does not flow from the batteries into the workshop.

3 1c, 2b, 3b, 4c, 5b

3 Cooling system

1 1 minus two degrees Fahrenheit
  2 twenty-one degrees Celsius
  3 seventy-five degrees Fahrenheit
  4 minus eight degrees Celsius
  5 twenty-four degrees Celsius
  6 thirty-three degrees Celsius

2 1 The water pump   6 Cool water
  2 Two hoses   7 The fan
  3 The thermostat   8 Cool water
  4 Hot water   9 The engine
  5 The fan

3 1 From the spring, water flows to a reservoir at the top of the hill.
  2 From the reservoir, water passes through a pipe to the field.
  3 The pipe goes into a field of fruit trees.
  4 Water leaves the pipe through small holes.
  5 The water then flows around the fruit trees.
  6 A little water flows out of the bottom of the field.
  7 This water enters a tank at the bottom of the hill.

4 Word list

1
1	enters	3	heats	5	sinks
2	flows	4	rises	6	leaves

2 1d, 2a, 3e, 4b, 5c

6 Materials

1 Materials testing

1
1. You can bend metal, but you can't bend wood.
2. You can heat air and you can heat water.
3. You can melt plastic, but you can't melt wood.
4. You can scratch glass and you can scratch metal.
5. You can stretch nylon, but you can't stretch glass.
6. You can break glass and you can break wood.
7. You can cut wood and you can cut metal.
8. You can compress air, but you can't compress glass.

2
1	are testing	5	is running
2	is sitting	6	is stretching
3	is tightening	7	is touching
4	is starting	8	Is the dummy's face striking

3
1. A: Are you pushing the handles?
   B: No, I'm rowing.
2. A: Is he walking?
   B: No, he's running.
3. A: Is she bending the wall bars?
   B: No, she's climbing the wall bars.
4. A: Are you pulling the bar down?
   B: No, I'm pushing the bar up.
5. A: Is he pushing the bar?
   B: No, he's picking the bar up.
6. A: Is she bending her legs?
   B: No, she's stretching her legs.

2 Materials and their properties

1 plastic, composite, fibreglass, titanium, concrete, ceramic, graphite, aluminium, steel, nylon, rubber, polystyrene, polycarbonate, diamond

2
1. A ceramic cup is heat-resistant and hard.
2. A concrete floor is rigid and tough.
3. A rubber tyre is flexible and strong.
4. A fibreglass window frame is heat-resistant and rigid.
5. A nylon rope is flexible and strong.
6. The graphite in the middle of a pencil is light and soft.
7. A polycarbonate road sign is rigid and strong.
8. A polystyrene coffee cup is brittle and light.

3
1. The nose cone is made of aluminium.
2. The wheels are made of aluminium alloy.
3. The tyres are made of rubber composite.
4. The frame is made of composite.
5. The inside is made of fibreglass.
6. The seats are made of plastic.
7. The engine is made of aluminium alloy.
8. The wings are made of aluminium alloy.

3 Buying

1 Product name: Backpack
Product no: 19/124
Quantity: one
Colour: green
Size: large
Material: polyester
Price: $125

2
1. jclarke@i-way.co.uk
2. alex2@anti-gm.org
3. s_hagen@renault.fr

3
1. bbc.co.uk/newsline
2. live-radio.net
3. sci-toys.com/prod/51

4
1. What's your surname, please?
2. Could you spell that, please?
3. What's your phone number, please?
4. What's your email address, please?
5. Could you repeat that, please?
6. How many helmets do you need?
7. What colour would you like?
8. And how do you want to pay?

4 Word list

1
1. The nose cone is made of fibreglass.
2. The wheels are made of aluminium alloy.
3. The frame is made of cromoly, a steel alloy.
4. The tyres are made of rubber composite.
5. The radiator is made of aluminium.
6. The engine is made of aluminium alloy.
7. The pistons are coated with ceramic.
8. The wings are made of polystyrene and fibreglass.

2
1	strong	3	soft	5	light
2	brittle	4	flexible		

Review Unit C

Section 1

1 **1**
1	that		**2**	6	here
2	here			7	This
3	are			8	How
4	thanks			9	about
5	OK			10	I'm

2
1. bending, climbing, heating, holding, pulling, pushing
2. cutting, dropping, gripping, running, sitting, swimming
3. diving, driving, leaving, moving, rising, striking

3
A: Is everything OK?
B: No. The engine's cooling system isn't working. The temperature of the water is rising.
A: Is the fan blowing air through the radiator?
B: Yes, the fan is fine.

A: Is the pump pushing water round the engine?
B: Yes, the pump is working.
A: Look! That clip on the bottom hose is loose. Water is running out of the hose. So the cold water is not going back to the engine. Tighten the clip.
B: Is the water running out of the hose now?
A: No. Check the temperature.
B: Ah! The temperature is dropping. Good!

Section 2

1 If you warm ice cubes, they melt.
If you pull a rubber band, it stretches.
If you strike a ceramic cup very hard, it breaks.
If you heat water to 100 °Celsius, it boils.
If you cool water, it sinks.
If you heat pieces of wood, they burn.

2

Part	Material	Properties
board	polystyrene, fibreglass	strong, light
mast	polycarbonate	strong, flexible
boom	aluminium, rubber	rigid, strong
sail	nylon, polyester	light, strong
rope	nylon	strong
daggerboard	polycarbonate	rigid
fin	polycarbonate	rigid
pivot	rubber	strong, flexible

7 Specifications

1 Dimensions

1 A: bridge, B: tunnel, C: road, D: cable, E: pylon, F: pier, G: deck, H: span

2 1 The sea has a depth of 270 metres.
2 The river is 25 metres deep.
3 The span is 330 metres long.
4 The pylons have a height of 160 metres.
5 The length of the road is 22 kilometres.
6 The deck has a width of 8 metres.

3 1 Where is this bridge?
It's in China.
2 How long is the inner span?
1490 metres.
3 How high are the pylons?
They're 215 metres high above the water.
4 How wide is the deck?
39.2 metres.
5 How high is the deck above the water?
50 metres.

2 Quantities

1 1 2003
2 40
3 metres
4 reinforced concrete
5 steel
6 aluminium

7 glass
8 area
9 square metres
10 18
11 metres per second
12 circle
13 small
14 wide

2

Item	Kind	Size	Product number	Quantity
Paint	green	10 litre tin	P176GR	4
Cement	white	20 kg bag	C0116W	5
Nails	packet of 50 / 100	24 / 30 mm	N420 / N240	None
Screws	packet of 100	24 mm	S00941	4

3 1 How much paint do you need?
2 What colour paint do you need?
3 What size tin do you need?
4 How much cement do you need?
5 How many bags do you need?
6 Do you have any screws?
7 How many screws do you need?
8 Do you need any nails?

3 Future projects

1

Gotthard Base Tunnel (GBT)	
Location of tunnel	in Switzerland, under the Alps
Possible completion date	2016–2017
Number of tunnels	2
Length of tunnels	57 kilometres
Depth below old tunnel	600 metres
Maximum speed of trains	250 kph
Source of power for trains	electricity
Number of trains per day	200–250

2 1 They're building a new tunnel.
2 There'll be two new tunnels.
3 They'll finish the tunnel in 2017.
4 The trains won't use magnetism.
5 There'll be more than 200 trains per day.

3 The GBT will be the longest <u>railway</u> tunnel in the world. It will connect Italy and <u>Switzerland</u>. Engineers will finish the project in <u>2017</u>. The new tunnel will be <u>below</u> the old railway tunnel. There will be <u>about 200–250</u> trains per day. The new trains will use <u>electricity</u>. <u>Some</u> of them will run at 250 kph.

4 Word list

1 length, height, width, depth

2 a bottle of oil
a tube of glue
a bag of cement
a packet of screws
a tin of paint

3
1 lay the foundations
2 build the piers
3 put the pylons on the piers
4 attach the cables to the pylons
5 make the deck
6 fix the deck to the cables
7 build the road

8 Reporting

1 Recent incidents

1 check, checked, checked
change, changed, changed
stop, stopped, stopped
plan, planned, planned
cut, cut, cut
put, put, put
buy, bought, bought
sell, sold, sold
send, sent, sent
fall, fell, fallen
speak, spoke, spoken
take, took, taken
write, wrote, written

2 A: Have you spoken to Security?
B: Yes, I have.
A: Good. Have you rung the new customer?
B: No, I haven't. I'll do it now.
A: Have you sent an email to HTB?
B: Yes, I have.
A: Good. Have you written the incident report?
B: No, I haven't. I'll do it now.

3
1 Hello? Police? A thief has taken my digger.
2 Police? A man has driven a digger into the town centre here.
3 Hello? A digger has crashed into a shop window in Broad Street.
4 Help! Two men have come into my shop in Broad Street.
5 One man has broken the display case with a sledgehammer.
6 The two thieves have stolen some diamonds.
7 Two men with bags have run down to the river.
8 The two men have jumped into a motor boat. They are on the river now.

2 Damage and loss

1
1 They have bent the router antenna.
2 The user manual is torn.
3 Someone has broken the camera.
4 The body of the radio is cracked.
5 The speakers are damaged.
6 Someone has cut the power cable.
7 The lenses of the goggles are scratched.
8 I have burnt the overalls.
9 They have dented the car door.

2

Order No: PC08/1020/0017	Item	Damaged	Missing
Name: Mr Burt Sandell	1 router antenna	bent	
Address: 14 Hayford Road	2 mouse		✓
Catford	3 computer screen	scratched	
London	4 keyboard	broken	
Postcode: SE10 4QY	5 power cable		no plug
Tel: 0208 411 4009	6 LH speaker	damaged	
Email: bsandell87@pdq.com	7 RH speaker	hole in front	
	8 user manual		✓

3 Reporting damage
1 The box is damaged.
2 The overalls are torn.
3 There's a dent on one of the speakers.
4 There are some cracks on the body of the radio.

Reporting something missing
1 The headphones are missing.
2 There are no pliers in the toolbox.
3 The power cable doesn't have a plug.
4 There are no batteries in the box.
5 The radio has no antenna.
6 There's no user manual in the box.

3 Past events

1
1 Which year did you travel to the ISS?
2 When did you take off?
3 How did you travel into space?
4 What did you take with you?
5 What did you do on the ISS?
6 Did you repair the solar panel?
7 When did you leave the ISS?
8 When did you land in the USA?

2
1 I bought it 10 months ago.
2 I dropped it 4 weeks ago.
3 I phoned the company 3 weeks ago.
4 I brought it into the Service Department 10 days ago.
5 I sent my email 3 days ago.
6 I received your bill 2 days ago.
7 I rang 10 minutes ago.

4 Word list

1
buy / bought
drive / drove
fall / fell
fly / flew
go / went
lose / lost
put / put
sell / sold
send / sent

speak / spoke
steal / stole
take / took
write / wrote
break / broke
bend / bent
burn / burnt
cut / cut
tear / tore

2
1 insulation
2 scaffolding
3 sledgehammer
4 hard hat
5 crane
6 digger
7 goggles
8 overalls

Review Unit D

Section 1

1
1	long	7	length	13	width
2	wide	8	more than	14	length
3	depth	9	at	15	below
4	through	10	deep	16	through
5	more than	11	long		
6	depth	12	wide		

2
1 A: Hello. Can I help you?
B: Yes. I'm building a wall and I need some cement.
A: How much do you need?
B: I need two bags please. And I also need some sand.
A: How many bags do you need?
B: I need six bags, please.

2 A: Hello. What can I do for you?
B: Do you have any paint?
A: Yes. How much do you need?
B: 10 litres, please. And I need some nails.
A: How many packets?
B: One packet, please.

Section 2

1

Verb	Past simple	Past participle
bend	bent	bent
build	built	built
burn	burnt	burnt
find	found	found
lose	lost	lost
pay	paid	paid
break	broke	broken
come	came	come
give	gave	given
go	went	gone

2
1 When did the digger drive into the shop window?
2 When did the thieves break into the office?
3 How much money did the mechanic find?
4 When did the builders take off the old roof?
5 Where did the scaffolding fall down?

3
A: Have you put up the scaffolding?
B: Yes, I have.
A: Good. Have you changed the power cable?
B: No, I haven't. I'll do it next week.
A: Have you bought the bricks?
B: No, I haven't. I'll do it next week.
A: Have you spoken to the supplier?
B: Yes, I have.
A: Good. Have you ordered the water tank?
B: No, I haven't. I'll do it next week.

9 Troubleshooting

1 Operation

1
1	supports	4	drives	7	propels
2	steers	5	pulls	8	release
3	controls	6	pushes		

2
1 What does the engine do?
It drives the impeller.
2 What does the impeller do?
It pulls water in and pushes it out.
3 What do the handlebars do?
They steer the craft.
4 What do the levers do?
They control the speed of the craft.
5 What does the seat do?
It supports the rider.

3
1 The seat is mounted on the body.
2 The handlebars are mounted on the body.
3 The levers are attached to the handlebars.
4 The engine is mounted on the body.

2 Hotline

1
1	display	3	speaker	5	adapter
2	mouse	4	disk drive	6	power switch

2
Dialogue 1: 2 mistakes
Dialogue 2: 0 mistakes
Dialogue 3: 1 mistake

3
1 The display is open.
2 The power switch is down.
3 The mouse is connected.
4 The speaker is disconnected.

4
1 No, it doesn't.
2 Is the power switch down?
No, it isn't.
3 Are the loudspeakers connected?
No, they aren't.
4 Is the adapter connected?
Yes, it is.
5 Do the loudspeakers work?
No, they don't.
6 Are the two LED lights on?
Yes, they are.
7 Does the computer start?
Yes, it does.
8 Do the loudspeakers work now?
Yes, they do.

3 User guide

1
Open, Press, check, recharge, work, press, Close

2
1 If the LEDs aren't on, check the battery.
2 If the printer doesn't work, connect it to the adapter.
3 If the printer light isn't on, push the 'On' button.
4 If the batteries are old, replace them.

5 If the speakers don't work, connect them to the computer.

6 If it prints in black, press the button for 'Start Colour'.

3
1	Check	5	plug	9	unplug
2	plugged	6	Press	10	Press
3	Check	7	shuts	11	turns
4	connected	8	shut		

4 Word list

1 adapter, battery, computer, disk, disk drive, display, key, laptop, LED, modem, mouse, notebook computer, power button, power outlet, power source, router, screen, speaker, start button, switch

2
1 The rider releases the lever.
2 The fan pulls air in.
3 The rider can go backwards.
4 The engine is below the platform.
5 The fan stops and the airboard goes downwards.

10 Safety

1 Rules and warnings

1
1 safety helmet   3 safety boots
2 safety gloves   4 safety goggles

2
1 Don't smoke in the workshop.
2 Never use mobile phones in the workshop.
3 You must wear safety goggles when you use this machine.
4 You must never enter the cold store if you are alone in the factory.
5 Do not lift heavy weights by hand.
6 You mustn't use this machine without the guard.
7 Always read the manual before you service the machine.
8 Don't touch packets in the cold store without gloves.

3
1 drop / break   5 pick / burn
2 put / melt   6 touch / get
3 lift / hurt   7 use / trap
4 use / scratch

2 Safety hazards

1
1 There is some liquid on the floor.
2 There is a hole in the outside door.
3 There is no fire exit.
4 There is a broken window.
5 There are some cables on a workbench.
6 There are no fire extinguishers in the factory.
7 There are two machine guards missing.
8 There are some damaged warning cones.

2
1 You could start a fire.
2 You might get an electric shock.
3 You could trip over them.
4 You might trap your hair in it.
5 You could fall into it.

6 You might injure your head.
7 You could burn your hand.

3
1 There were no fire extinguishers anywhere in the factory.
2 There was some food and drink on the workbenches.
3 There were some boxes of parts on the stairs.
4 The guard on one of the machines was broken.
5 There was some oil on the floor.
6 Two of the windows were broken.
7 The fire exit was locked with a padlock.
8 There was no key for the padlock.

3 Investigations

1

About the accident	Type of accident (tick)	About the injured person
Date: March 29th Time: 3.30 pm Location: No. 6 workshop	[✓] injured self [ ] injured somebody else [ ] slipped, tripped or fell [✓] lifted something [✓] dropped something	Name: Peter Graski Job title: Storeman Injury: Hurt his back and foot At work: No

2
1 First, where did the accident happen?
2 Was anybody hurt?
3 When did it take place?
4 What's the name of the injured person?
5 What does he do?
6 What's his job?
7 Did he injure anybody else?
8 What happened?

3
1	on	6	on	10	between
2	in	7	with	11	away
3	into	8	on	12	into
4	in	9	on	13	out
5	of				

4 Word list

1
1 dense cloud   5 circular saw
2 bare hand   6 electric shock
3 lighted match   7 high-voltage
4 near miss

2
1 fire extinguisher   5 flight path
2 safety boot   6 mobile phone
3 safety hazard   7 building site
4 sea level

3 altitude, aviation, cloud, distance, emergency, type, anti-collision system, flight path, near miss, sea level

Review Unit E

Section 1

1
1	cushion	4	skirt	7	fibreglass
2	engine	5	platform	8	levers
3	fans	6	body	9	acceleration

2
1	can	5	is	9	have
2	doesn't	6	is	10	haven't
3	I've	7	have	11	does
4	there's	8	have	12	does

3
1 Turn the key to the right. Press the starter button.
2 If the engine starts, move the lever to 'D'. Ride away.
3 If the engine doesn't start, check the battery.
4 If the battery works, check the starter motor.
5 If the battery doesn't work, recharge the battery.
6 If the battery doesn't work, replace the battery.

Section 2

1
1 Turn off this machine after use.
2 Always use safety boots in the shipyard.
3 Drivers must report to the office.
4 Never ride on the forklift truck.
5 Do not use this machine without safety goggles.
6 You must not reverse without a supervisor.

2
1	inspected	10	was
2	found	11	came
3	were	12	moved
4	was	13	hit
5	didn't have	14	was
6	were	15	shouted
7	was	16	saw
8	were	17	wasn't
9	lifted		

3
1 Where did the incident happen?
2 When did it take place?
3 Did it take place on a ship?
4 What did the crane lift?
5 Was there a rope attached to the beam?
6 Did the beam hit the worker?
7 Was the worker hurt?

11 Cause and effect

1 Pistons and valves

1
1	handle	7	piston	13	tank
2	lever	8	downpipe	14	float ball
3	piston	9	float ball	15	inlet valve
4	tank	10	tank	16	tank
5	downpipe	11	float arm	17	inlet pipe
6	handle	12	inlet valve		

2
allow it to do
cause it to do
let it do / make it do
prevent it from doing / stop it from doing

3
1 The pump causes the water to flow along the pipes.
2 The valves let air enter the tyres.
3 The valves prevent air (from) escaping from the tyres.
4 The sun makes the solar panel heat the water.
5 The cooling system stops the engine (from) getting very hot.
6 The closed inlet valve doesn't allow the water to flow out.

2 Switches and relays

1
1	switch	7	terminal
2	switch	8	catch
3	terminal	9	moving contact
4	electromagnet	10	fixed contact
5	moving contact	11	switch
6	fixed contact		

2 1c, 2a, 3b

3
1 F Three of the systems cause an alarm to sound.
2 T
3 The ExitGuard works when somebody breaks open the ExitGuard.
4 T
5 The burglar alarm works on the doors and windows.
6 T

3 Rotors and turbines

1
1	gear	4	blade	7	controller
2	brake	5	turbine	8	anemometer
3	housing	6	shaft	9	rotor

Vertical word: generator

2
1	turbine	6	blade
2	anemometer	7	generator
3	controller	8	shaft
4	brake	9	housing
5	gear	10	rotor

3 1b, 2a, 3c, 4a, 5b

4 Word list

1
1	prevent	5	transmit
2	expand	6	outlet
3	decrease	7	low pressure
4	blow	8	high-speed

2
1	beep	5	dial tone
2	horn	6	siren
3	alarm bell	7	buzzer / door bell
4	click		

12 Checking and confirming

1 Data

1 speed, motors, antennas, instruments, diameter, laser gun, tools, suspension, mast, wheels, titanium, robot, body, cameras, mud

2
1	on	4	on	7	to	10	in
2	over	5	near	8	at	11	up to
3	at	6	around	9	from	12	at least

3
1 What is the underwater robot called?
2 What is the weight of *Jason*?
3 Where are the two robot arms?
4 How does it collect living things?
5 Where are the special tools?
6 How many dives has *Jason* made?

2 Instructions

1 1d, 2a, 3e, 4b, 5c

6g, 7j, 8f, 9h, 10i

2
1 A car goes forwards and backwards.
2 A helicopter flies up and down.
3 A motorboat goes forwards and backwards.
4 A plane flies up and down.
5 A rover goes over rocks and holes.
6 A shuttle flies into space.
7 A truck goes forwards and backwards.

3
1	isn't moving	6	am pulling
2	isn't coming	7	is happening
3	am bringing	8	is coming
4	is happening	9	is sitting
5	Is the craft moving		

3 Progress

1
1 Take the large wrench to the workshop.
2 Tighten the nuts on the supply pipe.
3 Attach the pump to the supply pipe.
4 Assemble the water pump.
5 Connect the valve to the pump.
6 Replace the valve.

2
1	Yes. May 17th.	5	Yes.
2	No. May 17th.	6	Yes.
3	Yes.	7	No. May 20th.
4	No. May 19th.	8	No. May 22nd.

3
1 They've removed the nose cone.
2 He hasn't taken a photo of the nose cone yet. He'll do it on May 17th.
3 They've inspected the fuel tank.
4 They haven't replaced the fuel pipe yet. They'll do it on May 19th.
5 He's attached the cables to the foot pedals.
6 He's installed the new valves.
7 They haven't lubricated the gears yet. They'll do it on May 20th.
8 They haven't tested the car yet. They'll do it on May 22nd.

4 Word list

1
1	dismantle	3	replace	5	less than
2	remove	4	include	6	under

2 laser beam, robot arm, six-wheel drive, science laboratory, suspension system, temperature range, waste tank

Review Unit F

Section 1

1
1 It makes the pressure inside the cylinder fall.
2 This allows a mixture of petrol and air to enter the cylinder.
3 This stops the fuel mixture (from) escaping.
4 This makes the pressure in the cylinder rise.
5 The spark plug lights the fuel and causes it to explode.
6 This lets the burnt fuel escape.

2
1	dam	4	turbine	7	electricity
2	gates	5	shaft	8	cables
3	blades	6	generator		

Section 2

1
1 The rover is 202 centimetres high.
2 It has a length of 365 centimetres.
3 It has a weight of 3050 kilograms.
4 It has a four-wheel drive.
5 The wheels are made of steel alloy.
6 The wheels are 52 centimetres in diameter.
7 It can move at a speed of up to 155 kilometres per hour.
8 It can operate in a temperature range from minus 40 degrees Celsius up to 55 degrees maximum.

2
1 Have you collected
2 collected
3 Have you repaired it yet?
4 haven't
5 repair it
6 connected
7 We'll do them
8 you replaced it yet
9 did that on
10 Have you assembled it yet
11 assembled it on
12 replaced
13 doing
14 Have you serviced it yet
15 'll service it on